PROCESSION SOMBER
PAGEANT WALKED, SHUFFLED, LURCHI
TO UNCERTAINTY.

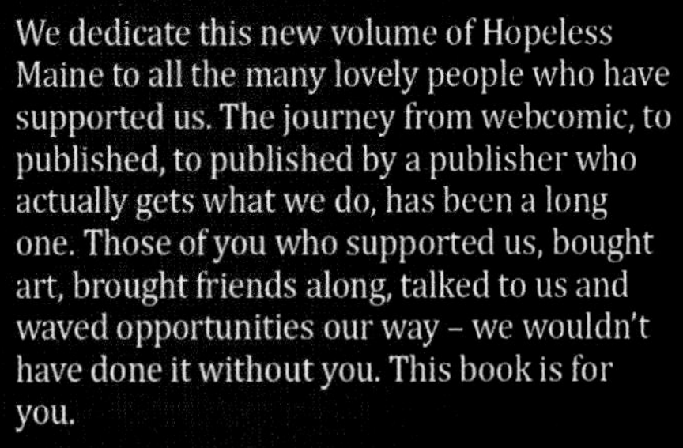

We dedicate this new volume of Hopeless Maine to all the many lovely people who have supported us. The journey from webcomic, to published, to published by a publisher who actually gets what we do, has been a long one. Those of you who supported us, bought art, brought friends along, talked to us and waved opportunities our way – we wouldn't have done it without you. This book is for you.

Thank you.

Masthead art by Jason Eckhardt
eck-art.tumblr.com

Design and layout by [illegible]
This volume gathers the contents of *Hopeless, Maine* Prelude - *The Blind Fisherman*, Book 1 - *Inheritance* and Book 2 - *Personal Demons*
Published by Sloth Publishing Limited, UK
Printed in the UK
ISBN: 978-1-908830-12-8

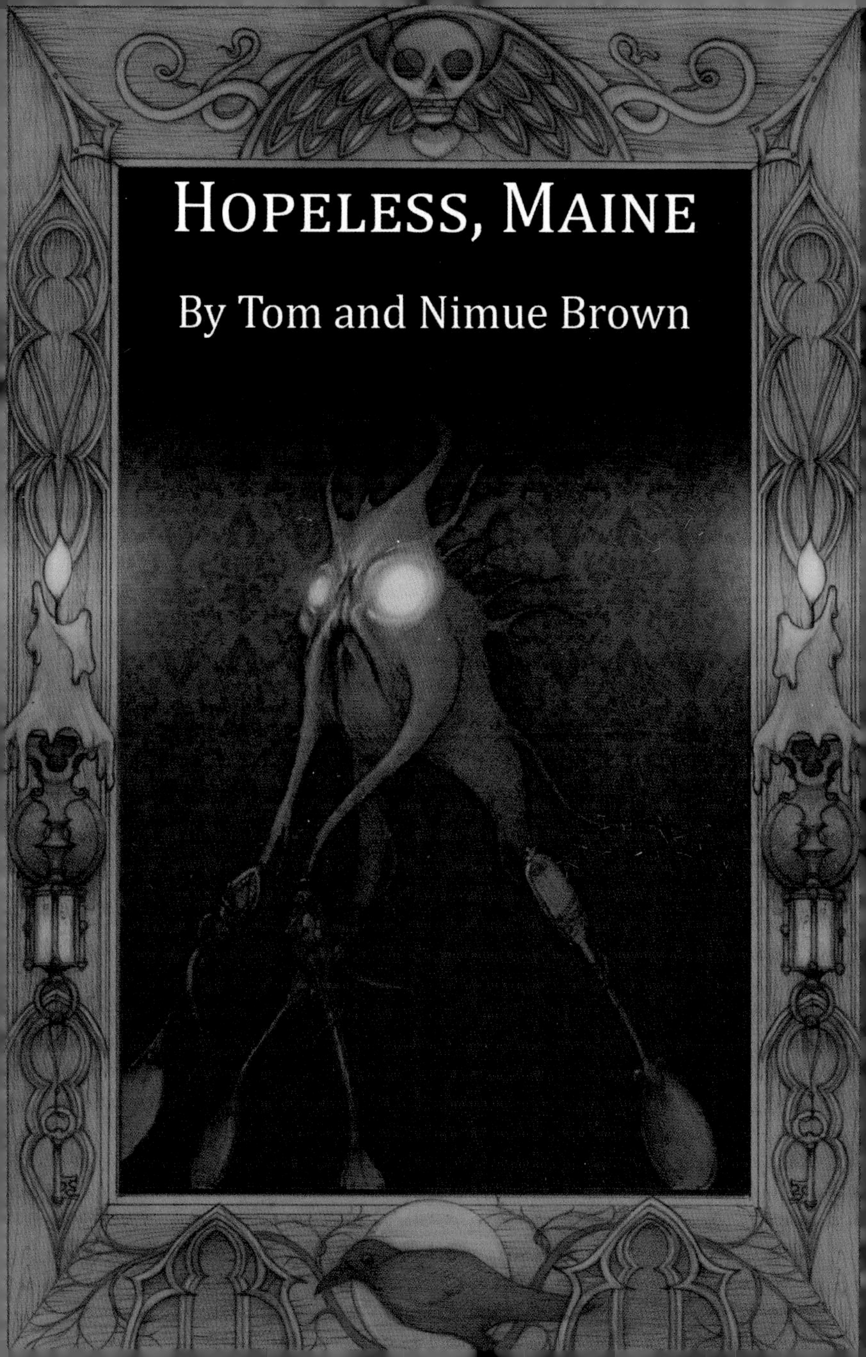
Hopeless, Maine
By Tom and Nimue Brown

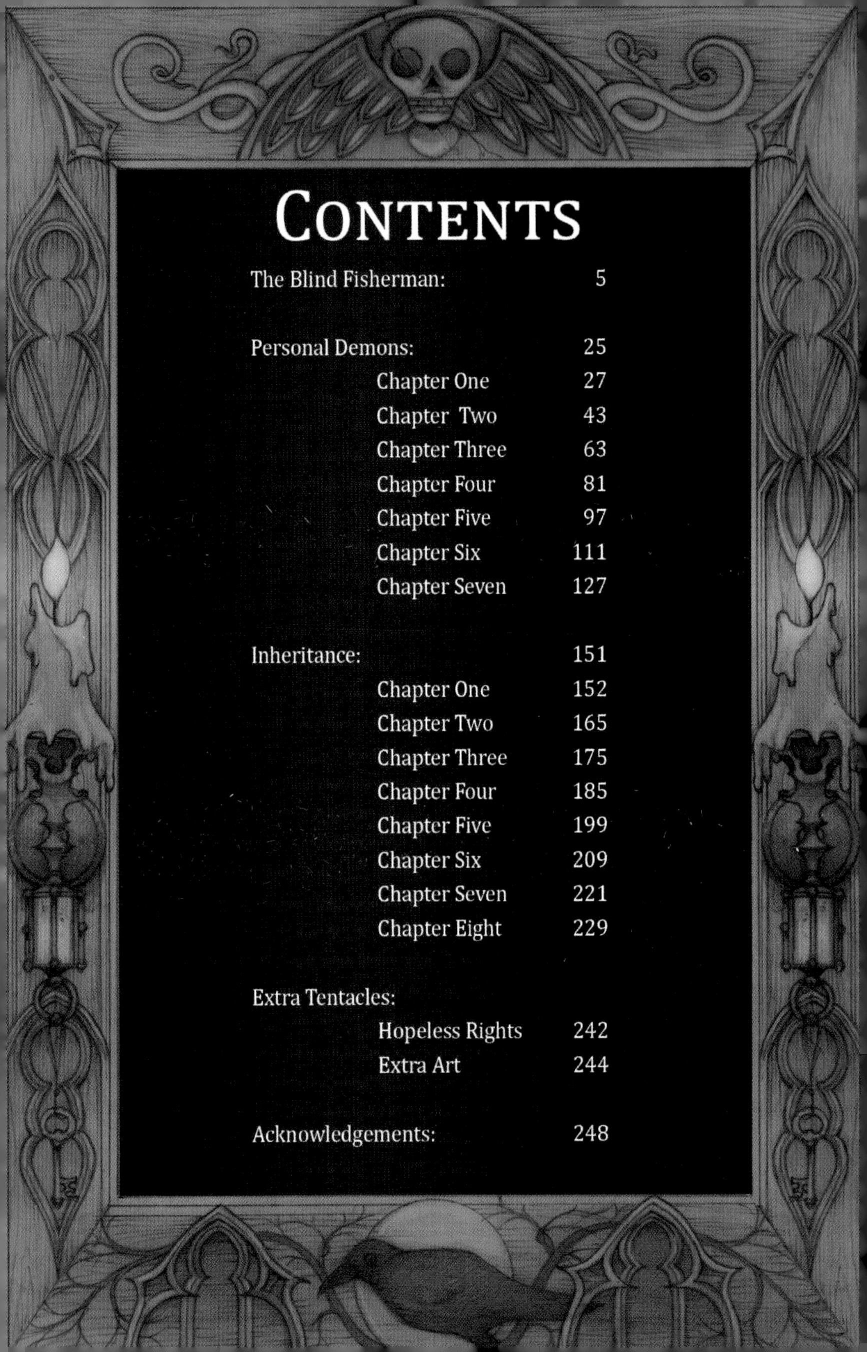

Contents

THE BLIND FISHERMAN
(A PRELUDE)

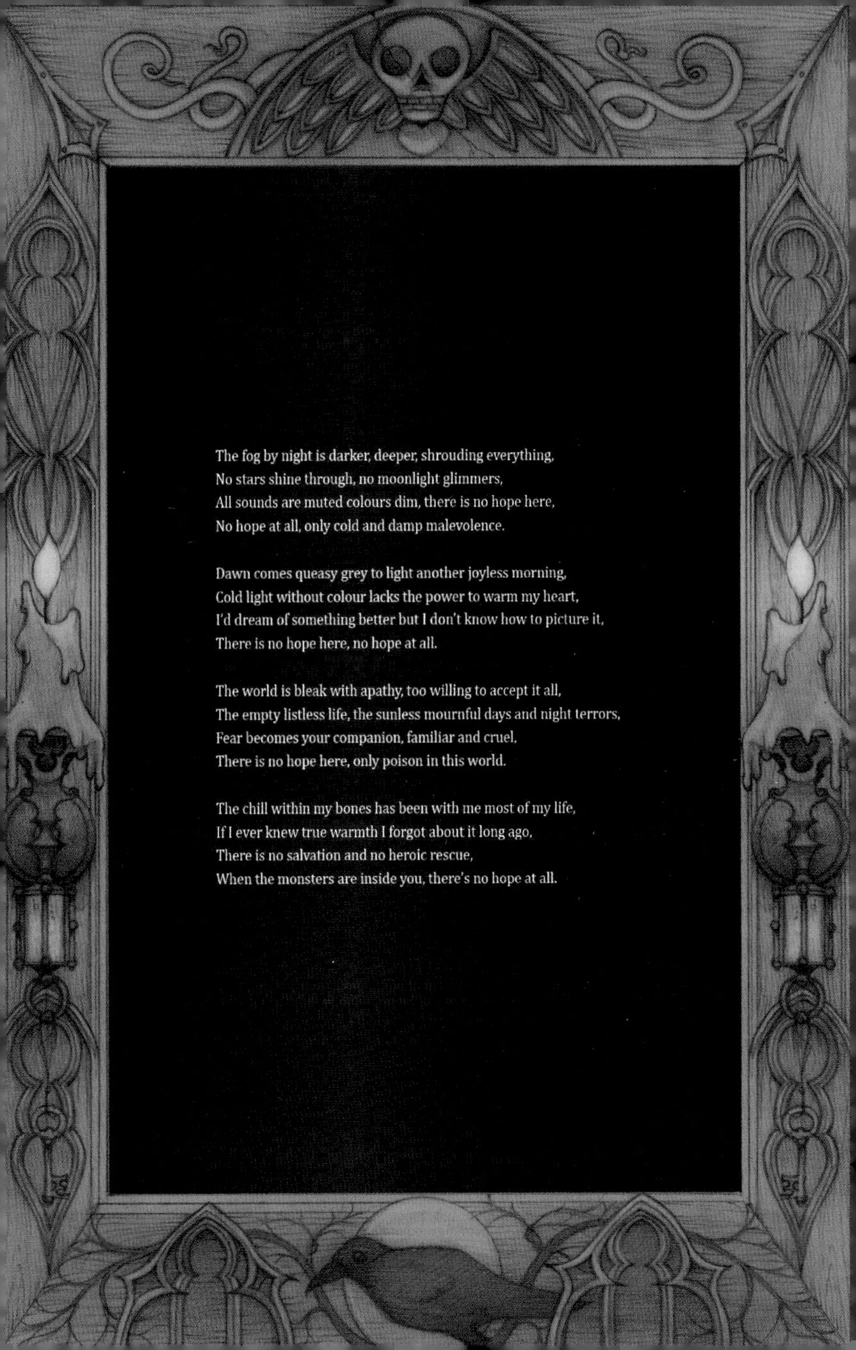

The fog by night is darker, deeper, shrouding everything,
No stars shine through, no moonlight glimmers,
All sounds are muted colours dim, there is no hope here,
No hope at all, only cold and damp malevolence.

Dawn comes queasy grey to light another joyless morning,
Cold light without colour lacks the power to warm my heart,
I'd dream of something better but I don't know how to picture it,
There is no hope here, no hope at all.

The world is bleak with apathy, too willing to accept it all,
The empty listless life, the sunless mournful days and night terrors,
Fear becomes your companion, familiar and cruel,
There is no hope here, only poison in this world.

The chill within my bones has been with me most of my life,
If I ever knew true warmth I forgot about it long ago,
There is no salvation and no heroic rescue,
When the monsters are inside you, there's no hope at all.

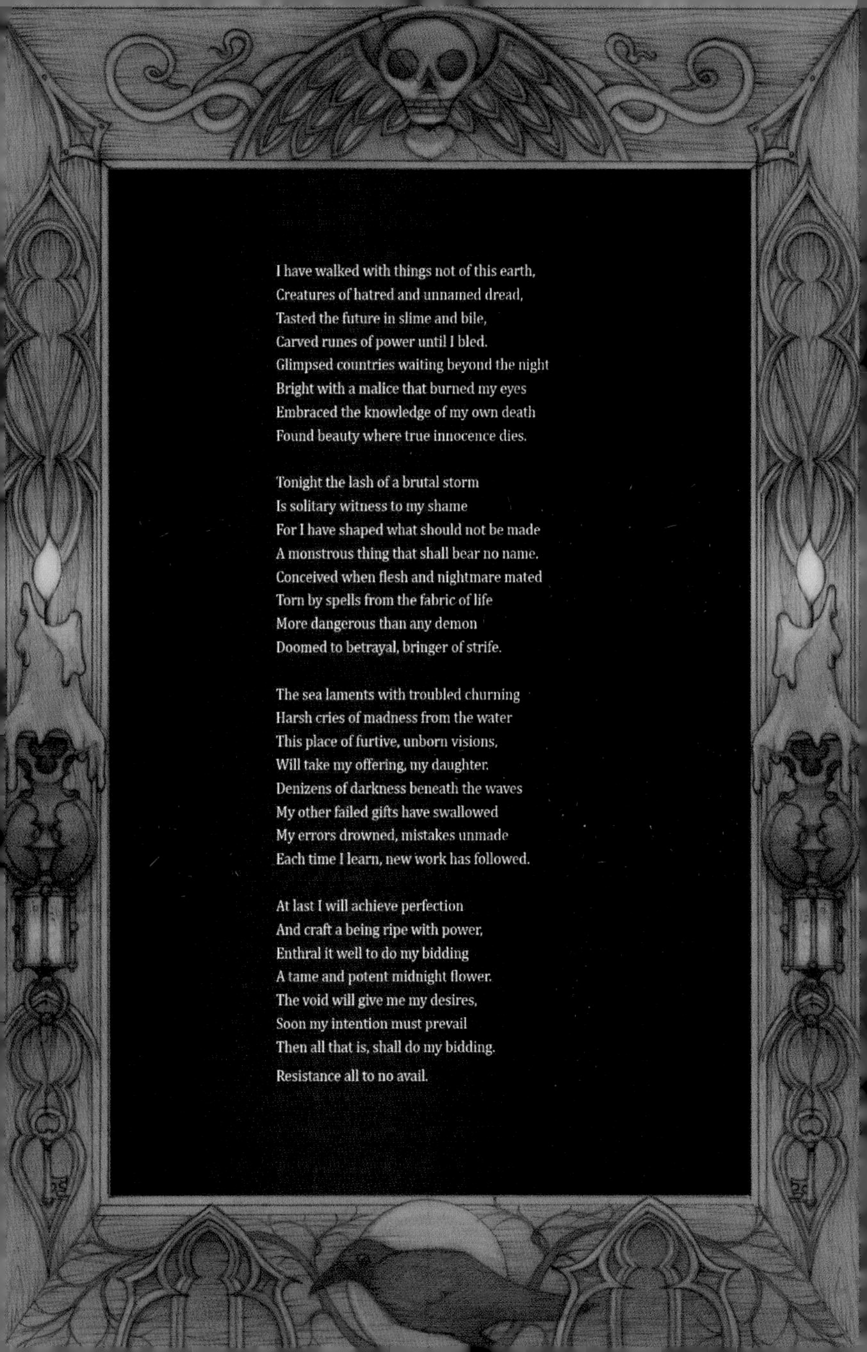

I have walked with things not of this earth,
Creatures of hatred and unnamed dread,
Tasted the future in slime and bile,
Carved runes of power until I bled.
Glimpsed countries waiting beyond the night
Bright with a malice that burned my eyes
Embraced the knowledge of my own death
Found beauty where true innocence dies.

Tonight the lash of a brutal storm
Is solitary witness to my shame
For I have shaped what should not be made
A monstrous thing that shall bear no name.
Conceived when flesh and nightmare mated
Torn by spells from the fabric of life
More dangerous than any demon
Doomed to betrayal, bringer of strife.

The sea laments with troubled churning
Harsh cries of madness from the water
This place of furtive, unborn visions,
Will take my offering, my daughter.
Denizens of darkness beneath the waves
My other failed gifts have swallowed
My errors drowned, mistakes unmade
Each time I learn, new work has followed.

At last I will achieve perfection
And craft a being ripe with power,
Enthral it well to do my bidding
A tame and potent midnight flower.
The void will give me my desires,
Soon my intention must prevail
Then all that is, shall do my bidding.
Resistance all to no avail.

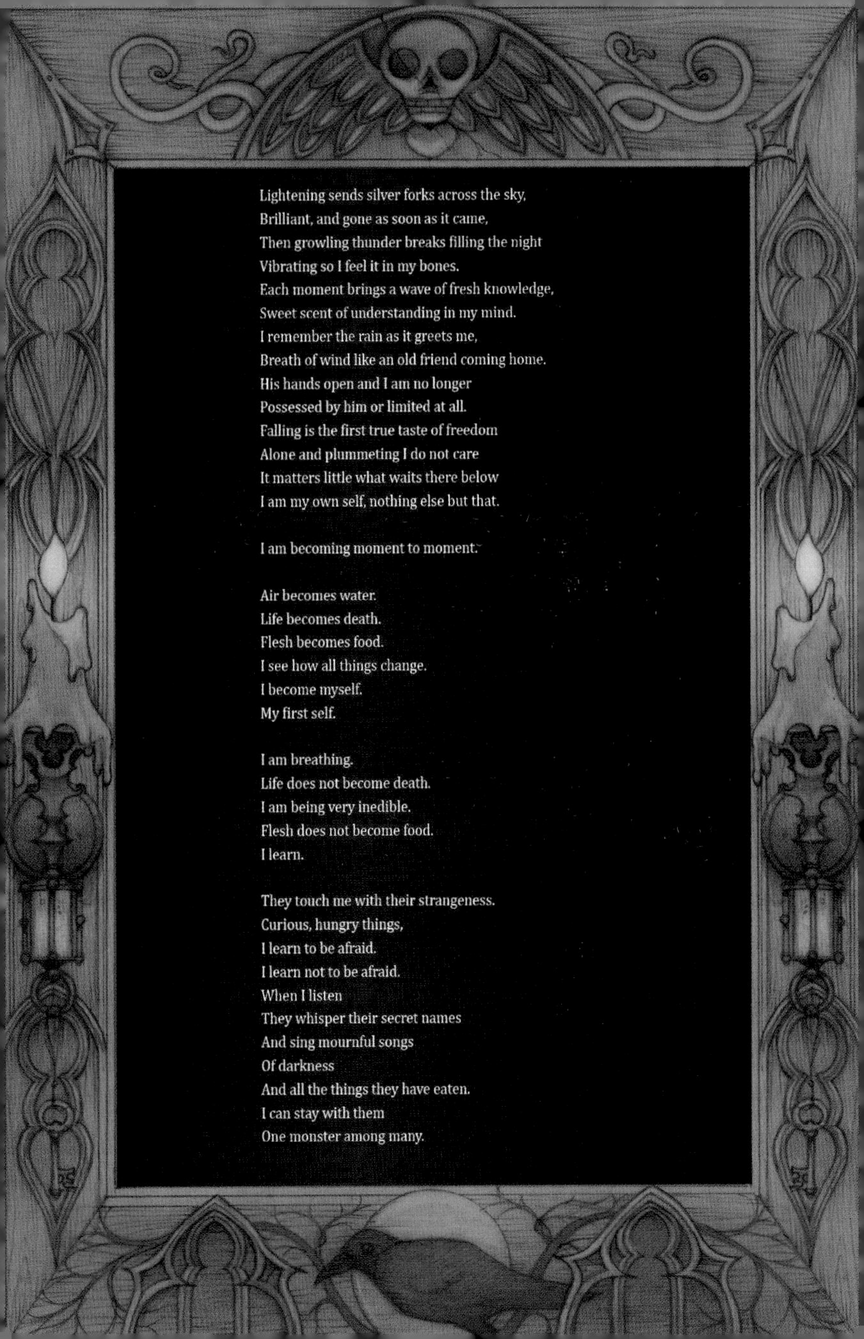

Lightening sends silver forks across the sky,
Brilliant, and gone as soon as it came,
Then growling thunder breaks filling the night
Vibrating so I feel it in my bones.
Each moment brings a wave of fresh knowledge,
Sweet scent of understanding in my mind.
I remember the rain as it greets me,
Breath of wind like an old friend coming home.
His hands open and I am no longer
Possessed by him or limited at all.
Falling is the first true taste of freedom
Alone and plummeting I do not care
It matters little what waits there below
I am my own self, nothing else but that.

I am becoming moment to moment.

Air becomes water.
Life becomes death.
Flesh becomes food.
I see how all things change.
I become myself.
My first self.

I am breathing.
Life does not become death.
I am being very inedible.
Flesh does not become food.
I learn.

They touch me with their strangeness.
Curious, hungry things,
I learn to be afraid.
I learn not to be afraid.
When I listen
They whisper their secret names
And sing mournful songs
Of darkness
And all the things they have eaten.
I can stay with them
One monster among many.

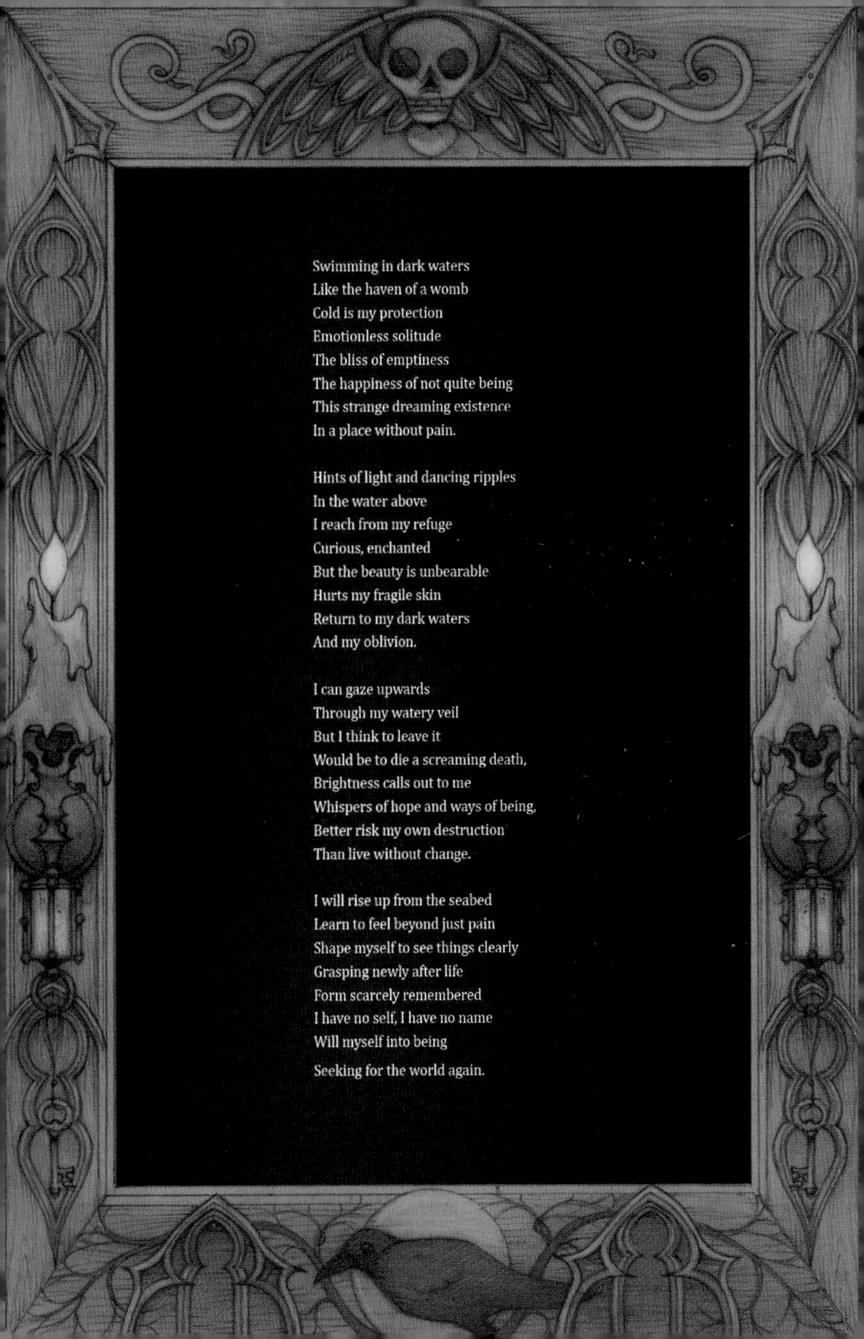

Swimming in dark waters
Like the haven of a womb
Cold is my protection
Emotionless solitude
The bliss of emptiness
The happiness of not quite being
This strange dreaming existence
In a place without pain.

Hints of light and dancing ripples
In the water above
I reach from my refuge
Curious, enchanted
But the beauty is unbearable
Hurts my fragile skin
Return to my dark waters
And my oblivion.

I can gaze upwards
Through my watery veil
But I think to leave it
Would be to die a screaming death,
Brightness calls out to me
Whispers of hope and ways of being,
Better risk my own destruction
Than live without change.

I will rise up from the seabed
Learn to feel beyond just pain
Shape myself to see things clearly
Grasping newly after life
Form scarcely remembered
I have no self, I have no name
Will myself into being
Seeking for the world again.

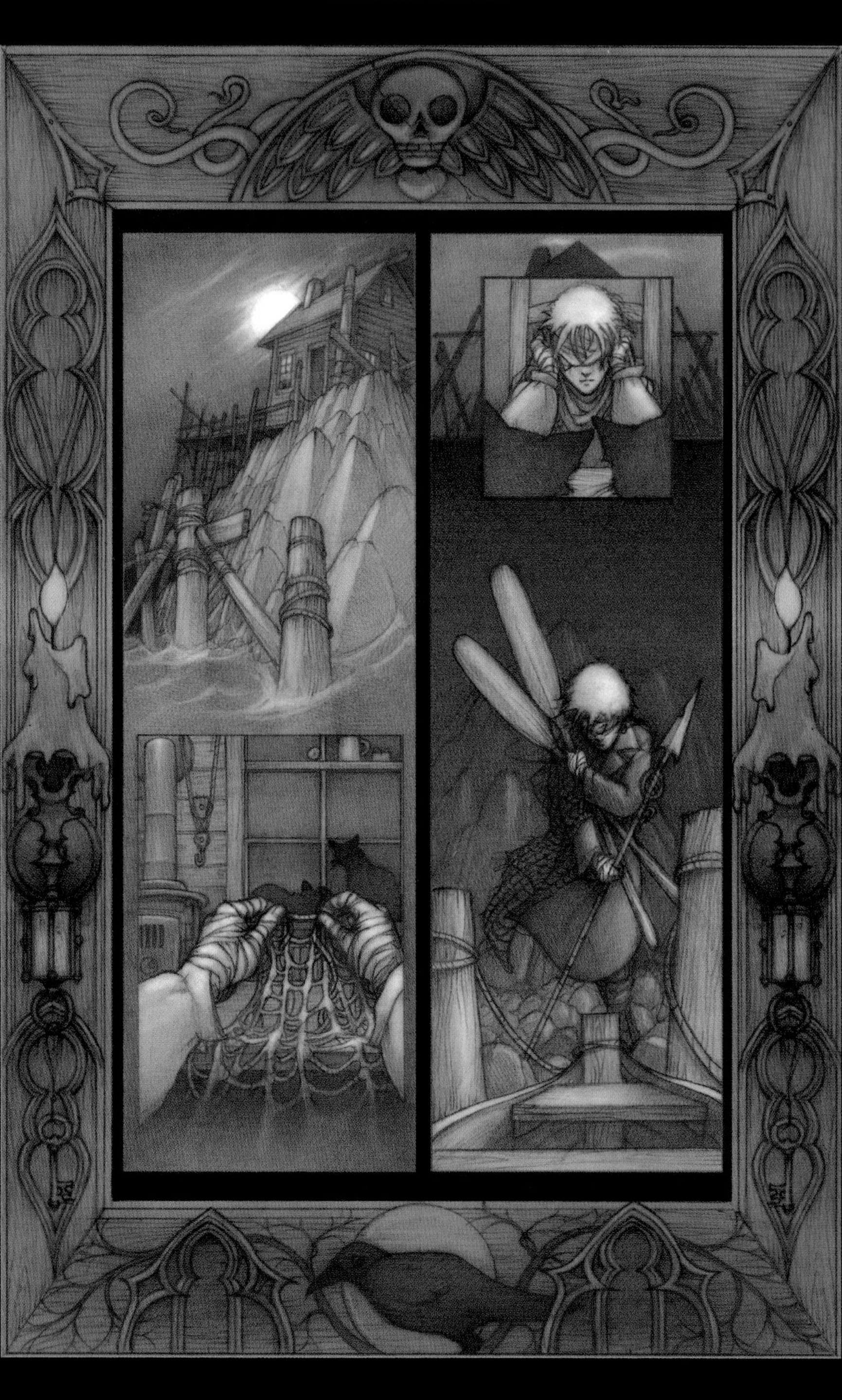

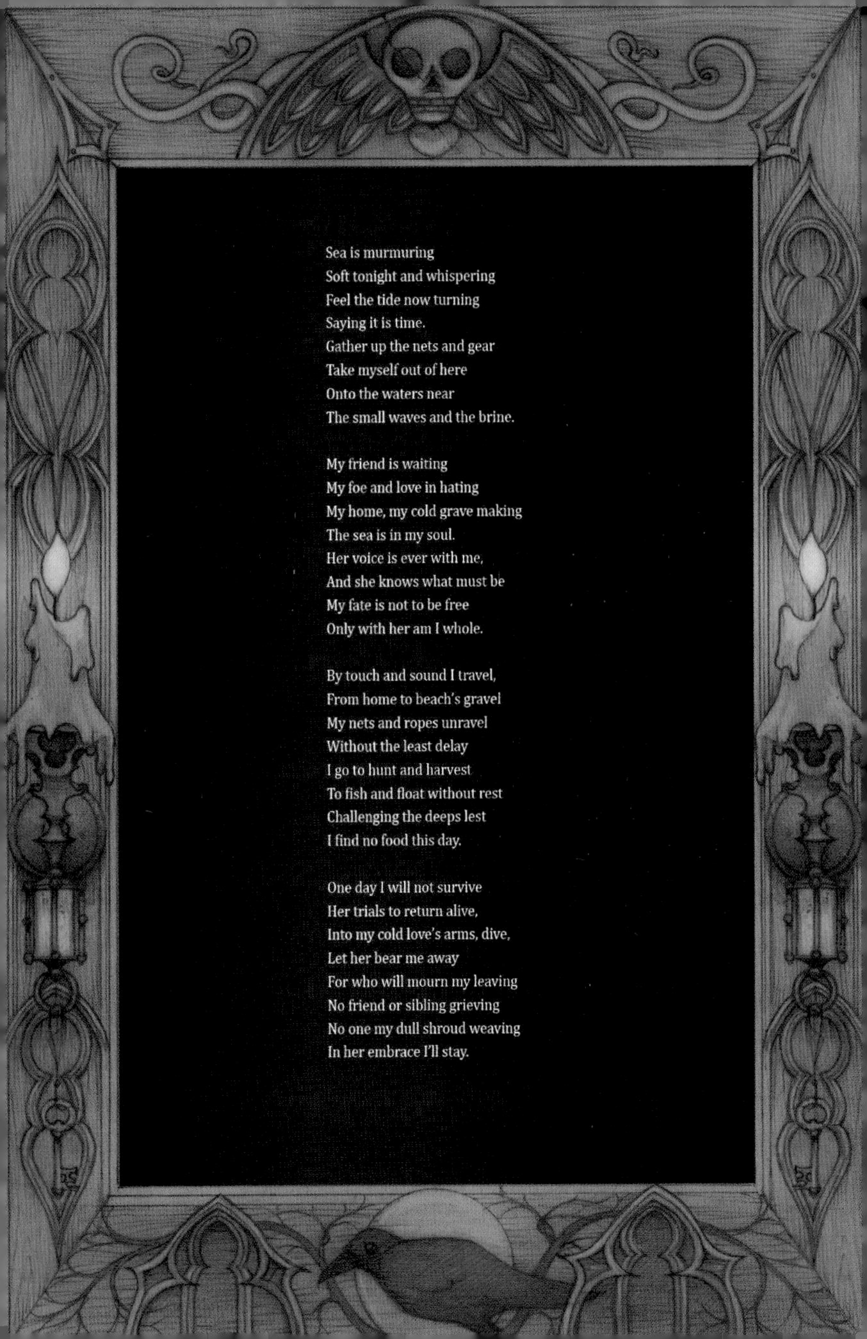

Sea is murmuring
Soft tonight and whispering
Feel the tide now turning
Saying it is time.
Gather up the nets and gear
Take myself out of here
Onto the waters near
The small waves and the brine.

My friend is waiting
My foe and love in hating
My home, my cold grave making
The sea is in my soul.
Her voice is ever with me,
And she knows what must be
My fate is not to be free
Only with her am I whole.

By touch and sound I travel,
From home to beach's gravel
My nets and ropes unravel
Without the least delay
I go to hunt and harvest
To fish and float without rest
Challenging the deeps lest
I find no food this day.

One day I will not survive
Her trials to return alive,
Into my cold love's arms, dive,
Let her bear me away
For who will mourn my leaving
No friend or sibling grieving
No one my dull shroud weaving
In her embrace I'll stay.

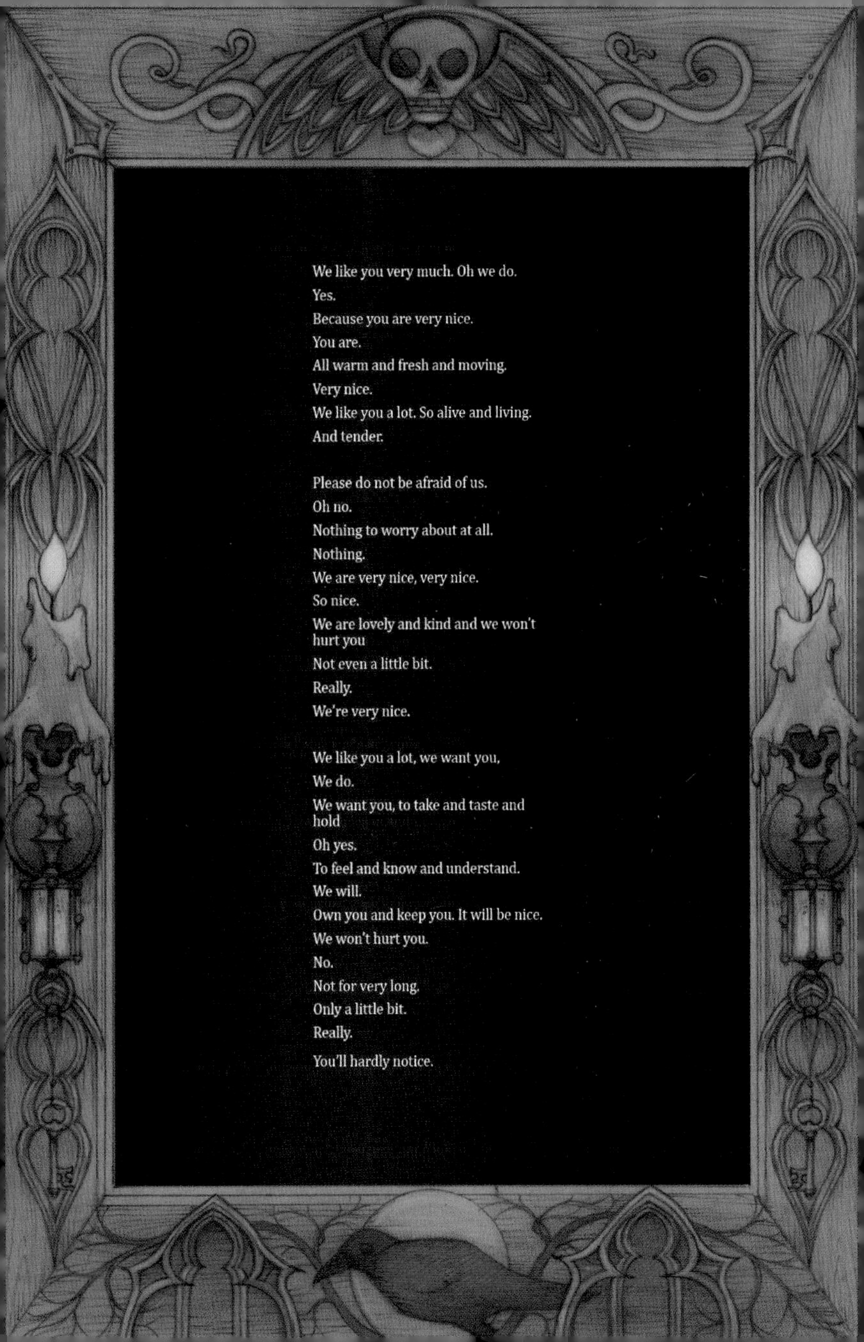

We like you very much. Oh we do.

Yes.

Because you are very nice.

You are.

All warm and fresh and moving.

Very nice.

We like you a lot. So alive and living.

And tender.

Please do not be afraid of us.

Oh no.

Nothing to worry about at all.

Nothing.

We are very nice, very nice.

So nice.

We are lovely and kind and we won't hurt you

Not even a little bit.

Really.

We're very nice.

We like you a lot, we want you,

We do.

We want you, to take and taste and hold

Oh yes.

To feel and know and understand.

We will.

Own you and keep you. It will be nice.

We won't hurt you.

No.

Not for very long.

Only a little bit.

Really.

You'll hardly notice.

Seeing is a distraction
In the muzzy halflight of my perceptions
Eyes lie, deny and mislead.

I have knowing beyond sight
Sensing the future before it touches me
Tasting bile before the wound.

In the web of life I hang
Spiderlike to feel the slightest of movements
Aware of the coming blow.

I walk the threads of living,
Moving with potential, possibility,
Fight against my own demons.

If there are others who see
Or know the fierce truth with subtle senses
They have never spoken it.

These hunts are the loneliest
I feel and I know what is beyond me,
The nightmare of it too real.

I go when I am summoned,
To sea or shore, to rocky height or woodland.
There are always new battles.

I shed my blood for strangers,
For those dependent on the meat I capture.
The horrors we feed upon.

I have no wish to see them,
Ignorance blesses me with some protection
From hunted and helped alike.

I live between sea and land
Between the different sides of fear and cruelty
Honouring the blood and pain.

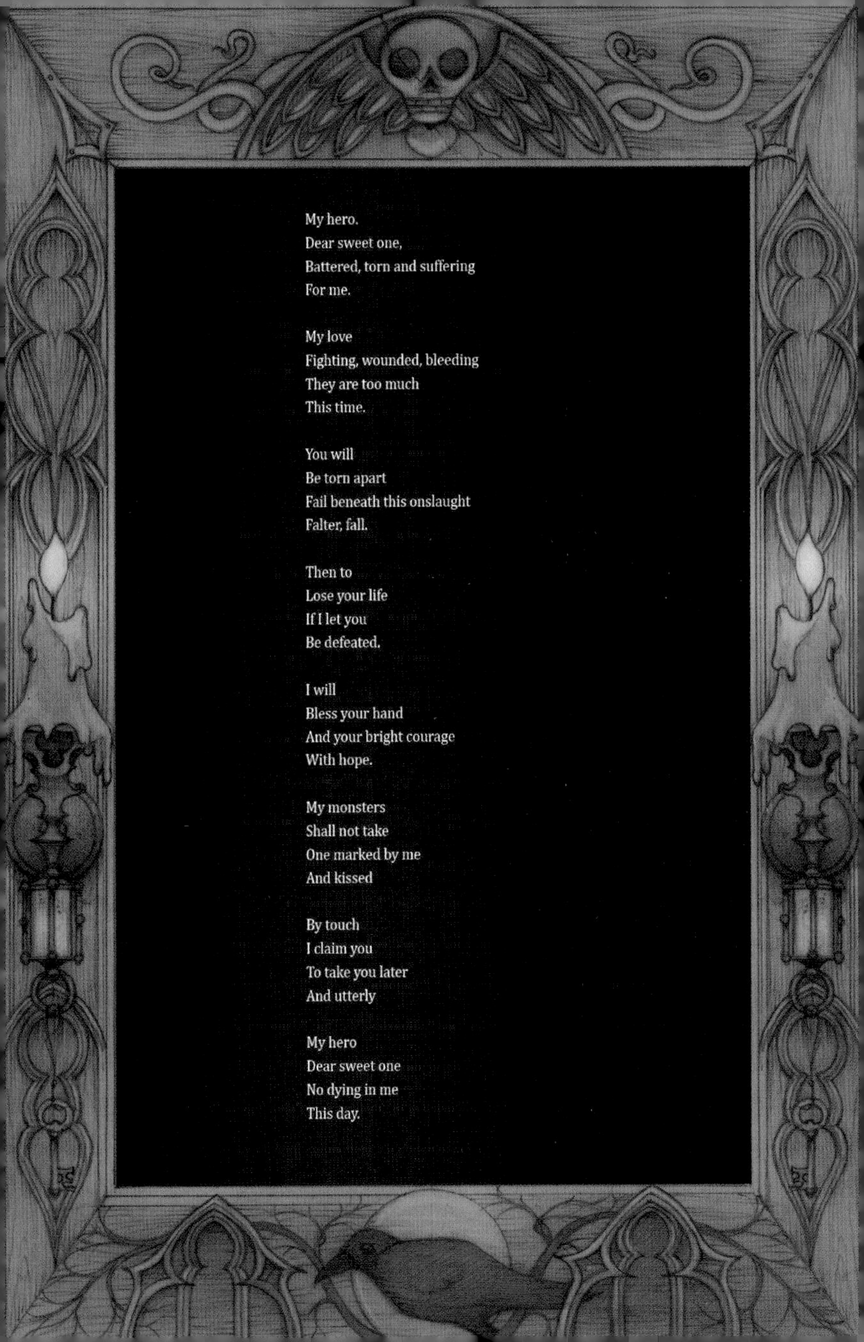

My hero.
Dear sweet one,
Battered, torn and suffering
For me.

My love
Fighting, wounded, bleeding
They are too much
This time.

You will
Be torn apart
Fail beneath this onslaught
Falter, fall.

Then to
Lose your life
If I let you
Be defeated.

I will
Bless your hand
And your bright courage
With hope.

My monsters
Shall not take
One marked by me
And kissed

By touch
I claim you
To take you later
And utterly

My hero
Dear sweet one
No dying in me
This day.

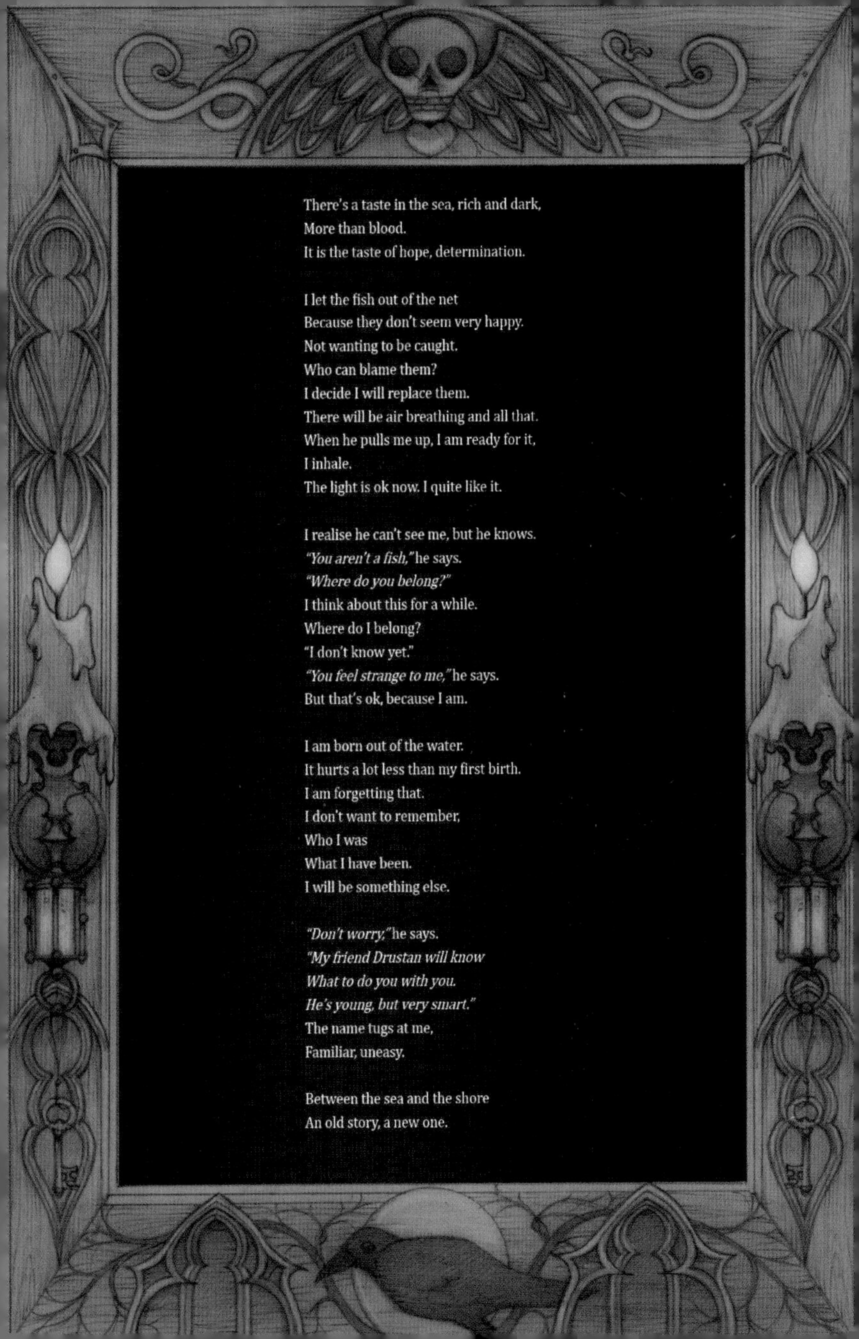

There's a taste in the sea, rich and dark,
More than blood.
It is the taste of hope, determination.

I let the fish out of the net
Because they don't seem very happy.
Not wanting to be caught.
Who can blame them?
I decide I will replace them.
There will be air breathing and all that.
When he pulls me up, I am ready for it,
I inhale.
The light is ok now. I quite like it.

I realise he can't see me, but he knows.
"You aren't a fish," he says.
"Where do you belong?"
I think about this for a while.
Where do I belong?
"I don't know yet."
"You feel strange to me," he says.
But that's ok, because I am.

I am born out of the water.
It hurts a lot less than my first birth.
I am forgetting that.
I don't want to remember,
Who I was
What I have been.
I will be something else.

"Don't worry," he says.
*"My friend Drustan will know
What to do you with you.
He's young, but very smart."*
The name tugs at me,
Familiar, uneasy.

Between the sea and the shore
An old story, a new one.

HOPELESS MAINE

BOOK ONE

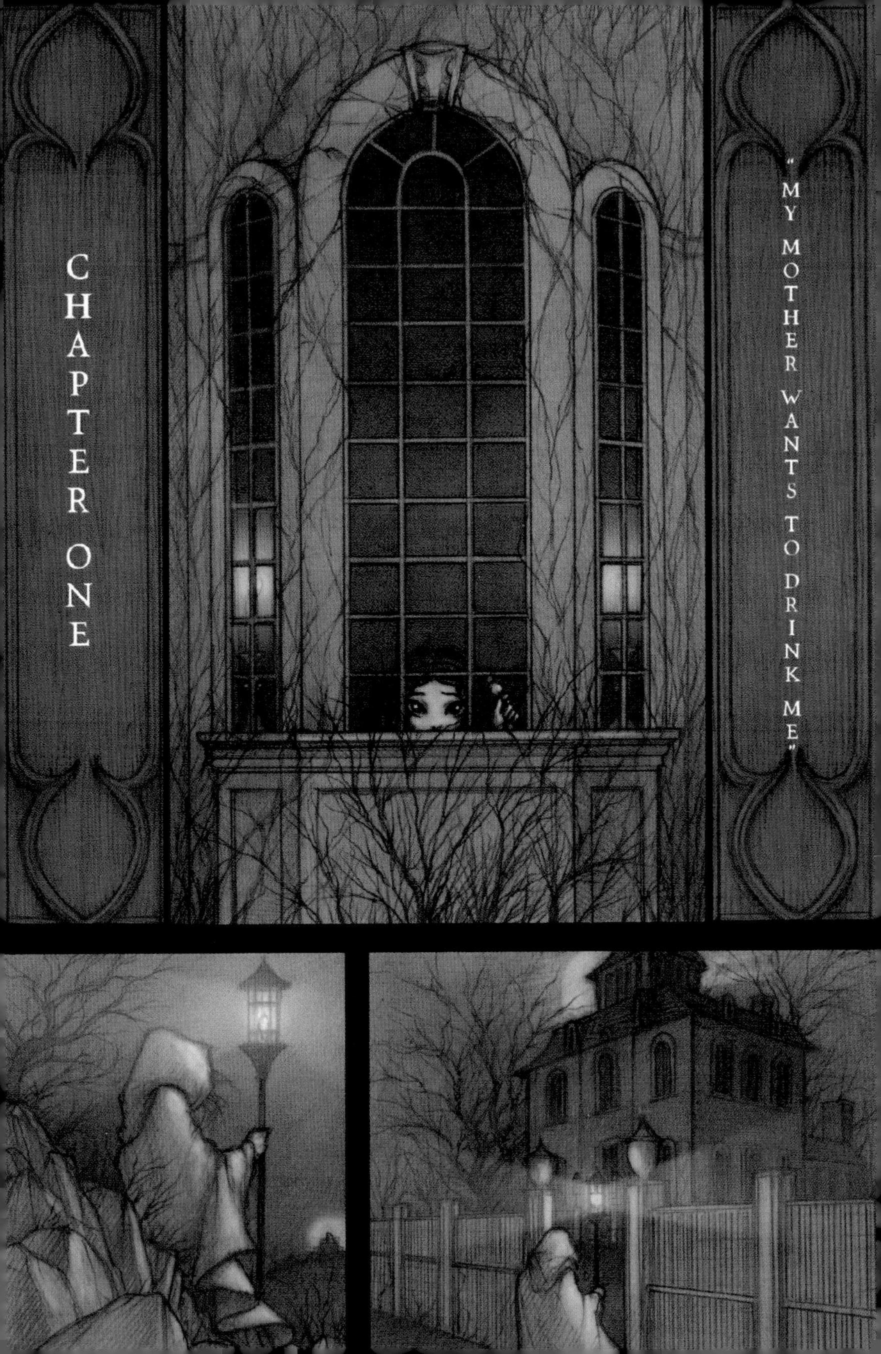
CHAPTER ONE
"MY MOTHER WANTS TO DRINK ME"

WHO IN HOPELESS CAN REMEMBER WHEN THEY LAST FELT THE SUN'S WARMTH ON THEIR SKIN?
TRAPPED ON AN ISLAND OFF THE COAST OF MAINE, THE PEOPLE OF HOPELESS FIND LIFE A LITTLE DARKER AND MORE DANGEROUS WITH EVERY DAY THAT PASSES.

THE NUMBER OF ORPHANS RISES CONTINUALLY, BUT WHAT HAPPENS TO THEIR PARENTS?
PLENTY OF THE BODIES ARE NEVER FOUND.
THIS IS NOT THE STUFF OF HAPPY, CARELESS CHILDHOODS; IT IS INSTEAD FERTILE GROUND FOR PERSONAL DEMONS.

IN HOPELESS, THE DEMONS ARE NOT ALWAYS ABSTRACT CONCEPTS.
SOME OF THEM HAVE VERY REAL TEETH, AND VERY REAL HORNS.

BANG
BANG
OPEN UP DUROSIMI! WE NEED TO TALK. NOW!
. . . .
CREAK

DUROSIMI? DON'T PLAY GAMES WITH ME.
I DON'T HAVE THE TIME ...
...OR THE INCLINATION FOR THAT MATTER.
MELISANDRA?
DRUSTAN?
SCUTTLE

KER-ACK
I KNOW YOU'RE IN HERE. SHOW YOURSELF TO ME.
NO.

WELL, YOU DON'T SOUND MUCH LIKE A DEMON, SO THAT'S A START.
WHERE'S DUROSIMI?
DON'T KNOW.

WHY DON'T YOU COME OUT WHERE I CAN SEE YOU PROPERLY?
NO.

I MIGHT HAVE A SWEET HERE.
SWOOSH
SCUTTLE
CRUNCH
SO, WHAT ARE YOU DOING HERE LITTLE GIRL?
I LIVE HERE.
UH HU.
ALL BY YOURSELF?
WHAT'S YOUR NAME?
SALAMANDRA.

YOU WERE SHOUTING NAMES.
YOU SHOUTED MY BROTHER'S NAME.
HE'S DEAD.
HE IS?
MY MOTHER KILLED HIM.
YOUR MOTHER?
SHE'S YOUR MOTHER?
MELISANDRA.
YEAH.
THEN YOU MUST BE...
AH.
OH
OH.
MY MOTHER WANTS TO DRINK ME.

AND YOUR FATHER'S THE SAME NO DOUBT. WELL, THAT EXPLAINS QUITE A FEW THINGS, DOESN'T IT?
SALAMANDRA, I THINK YOU'D BEST COME WITH ME.
NO.
I'LL FIND YOU SOME MORE SWEETS, MAYBE EVEN A NICE CAKE.
HAVE YOU GOT BROWNIES?
OF COURSE I HAVE.
OK THEN.

YOU CAN STAY HERE FOR A FEW DAYS.
THEN WHAT?
THAT'S THE QUESTION, ISN'T IT?
OH.
WHAT DO YOU WANT TO DO?
I DON'T KNOW, I WAS DOING OK.
YOU'RE A BIT SMALL TO BE LIVING ALL BY YOURSELF.
I LIKE LIVING AL BY MYSEL

IT'S NOT SAFE FOR SOMEONE AS YOUNG AS YOU THOUGH, IS IT?
ISN'T IT?

I FEEL QUITE SAFE.

HOW ABOUT YOU?

I THINK WE NEED TO FIND YOU SOMEWHERE TO LIVE SALAMANDRA.
NOT HERE.
DEFINITELY NOT HERE.
OH.

CHAPTER TWO

"IT MUST BE ONE OF DAD'S"

GOOD AFTERNOON MISS CALDER.
GOOD AFTERNOON MISS NIGHTSHADE. HOW CAN I HELP?

ONE ORPHAN.

OH, WHAT A SWEET LITTLE THING.
WHAT'S YOUR NAME PRECIOUS?
SALAMANDRA.
AND YOUR OTHER NAME...?
JUST SALAMANDRA
SHE MUST HAVE COME FROM SOMEWHERE.

I FOUND THE GIRL ABANDONED.
SHE CLEARLY HASN'T BEEN LOOKED AFTER AND SHE NEEDS A SAFE PLACE TO LIVE.

THEN I SUPPOSE YOU'D BETTER COME IN LITTLE ONE.

YOU AREN'T THE FIRST TO HAVE MISSING PARENTS.

I DON'T KNOW WHAT'S BECOMING OF THIS TOWN...

...TRULY I DON'T.

SO, WHO ARE YOUR PARENTS THEN?
YOU WILL ANSWER ME IN A POLITE AND TIMELY FASHION MY GIRL. WE DO NOT TOLERATE BAD MANNERS HERE.
I SEE.

SALAMANDRA IS NOT HAPPY.
SHE DOES NOT LIKE THE OTHER CHILDREN, AND SHE CAN SEE THAT THEY DO NOT LIKE HER.
NOTHING IS SAID. SHE IS DIFFERENT, THAT IS ALL.

THE ORPHANAGE SEEMS SO SMALL TO HER,
AND THERE ARE ALWAYS OTHER PEOPLE CLOSE BY.
SHE CAN HARDLY HEAR HER OWN THOUGHTS IN THIS PLACE.

HELLO?

WHO'S THERE?
PLEASE DON'T HURT ME!

IT'S ALL RIGHT, I WON'T HURT YOU.

OH, I'M SO GLAD.
I WAS SCARED.

WILL YOU LOOK AFTER ME?
SURE.

ARE YOU FROM THE ORPHANAGE?
YEAH. I'M RUNNING AWAY.

CAN I COME WITH YOU?

I SUPPOSE.
BUT IT MIGHT BE DANGEROUS.

I SUPPOSE YOUR PARENTS MUST BE DEAD THEN?

WAS IT VERY BAD, WHAT HAPPENED TO THEM?
PRETTY BAD, YES.

YOU MUST HAVE BEEN VERY UPSET.

WERE YOU SCARED?
A BIT.

AND NOW YOU'RE ALL BY YOURSELF, WITH NO ONE ELSE TO CARE ABOUT YOU ...
I'VE NEVER HAD A FRIEND BEFORE.
EXCEPT ME. I'LL BE YOUR FRIEND. I'LL CARE ABOUT YOU.
HAVEN'T YOU? THAT'S VERY SAD.
POOR YOU.
BUT YOU'VE GOT ME NOW.

WE CAN REST HERE, IT'S A GOOD PLACE. BETTER THAN BEING OUT IN THE NIGHT.
DO YOU LIVE HERE?

SOMETIMES.

WHERE DID YOU LIVE, WHEN YOU HAD A PROPER HOME?
I'LL SHOW YOU IF YOU LIKE.

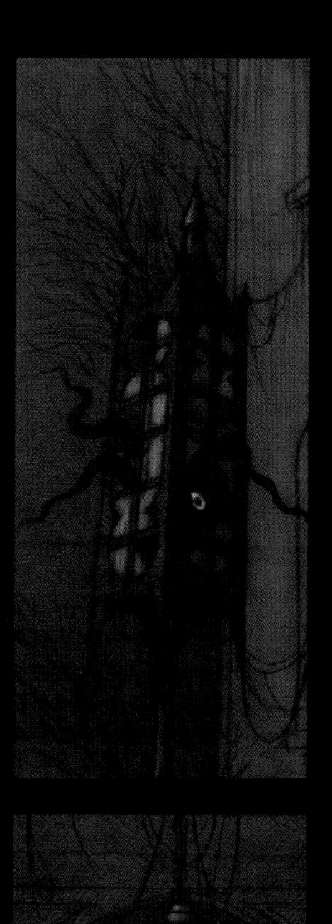

IS THIS REALLY YOUR HOUSE?
I GUESS.

COME AND HAVE A LOOK ROUND.

OH! WHAT IS IT?

WHAT DOES IT LOOK LIKE?

IT'S A DEMON.

A DEMON?
MUST BE ONE OF DAD'S.
YOU!

STOP IT!
LEAVE HER ALONE!
OR...?
I'LL MAKE YOU VERY SORRY.
I WARNED YOU.

I DON'T KNOW WHAT TO DO.

YOU CAN'T. I'M STUCK.
I'LL GET YOU DOWN.

BET?

HOW DID YOU DO THAT? WHAT ARE YOU?
IT'S JUST MAGIC.

YOU DO MAGIC?

A BIT, YEAH.

SHOW ME SOME MORE! PLEASE. MAKE ME FLOAT AGAIN OR SOMETHING.

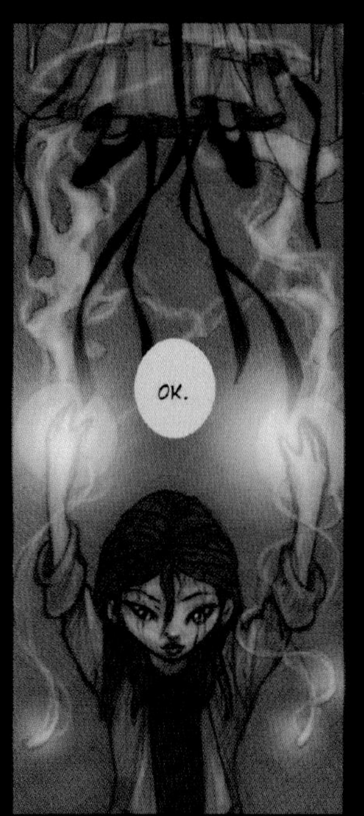
OK.

SO WHAT ELSE CAN YOU DO?
I CAN MAKE FIRE...

...WATCH!

WOW. THAT'S REALLY NEAT. WHAT ELSE?
I'M PRETTY GOOD AT MOVING THINGS AND BURNING STUFF. I HAVEN'T TRIED MUCH ELSE YET.
AND YOU EXPLODED THE DEMON.
OH YEAH, THAT TOO.
I TURNED ONE INSIDE OUT ONCE ...
... THAT WAS RATHER MESSY THOUGH.
CAN YOU DO ANYTHING YOU WANT?
I DON'T KNOW. I HAVEN'T FOUND ANYTHING I WANTED AND COULDN'T DO YET.

SO AREN'T THERE ANY LIMITS AT ALL?
I HAVE TO THINK VERY HARD ABOUT WHAT I WANT ...

... AND WHEN I GET TIRED, THINGS GO WRONG.

CHAPTER THREE

BUT WHERE WOULD WE GO?

THERE'S A WHOLE WORLD OUT THERE. WE COULD GO ANYWHERE WE LIKED. THIS IS A HORRIBLE PLACE.

DON'T YOU WANT TO LIVE SOMEWHERE ELSE?
I'M NOT SURE HOW TO DO THIS.

THERE'S A BOAT OVER THERE...

...WE COULD TAKE IT.

HMM. I'M NOT SO SURE ABOUT THIS.

IT'S JUST FOG. YOU COULD MAKE IT GO AWAY.

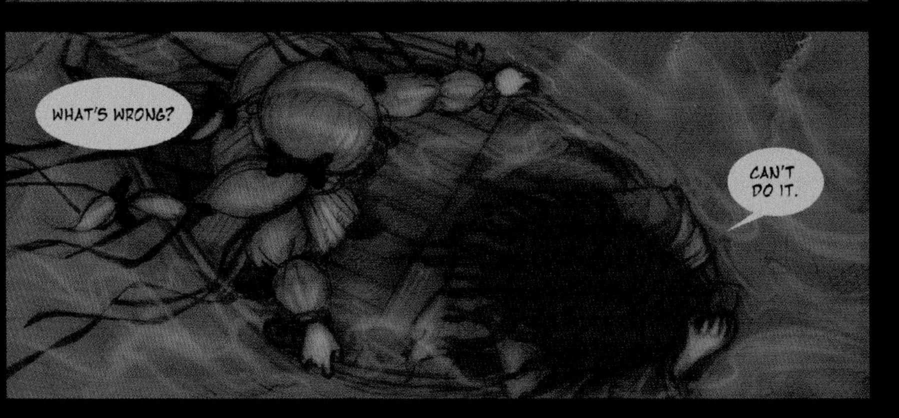
WHAT'S WRONG?
CAN'T DO IT.

IS ANYONE ELSE MISSING SOPHIE?
ONE OF THE GIRLS.
DON'T TELL ME, IT'S THE NEW ONE.
IT'S NOT HER FAULT. I'M SURE IT ISN'T.
WHO IS SHE? OR PERHAPS I SHOULD ASK, WHAT IS SHE?
DON'T SAY THAT. SHE'S JUST A CHILD.
SO TELL ME WHAT THIS MESS MEANS?

I THOUGHT YOU COULD DO ANYTHING.
POOR, POOR SALAMANDRA.

YOU AREN'T AS STRONG AS YOU THOUGHT YOU WERE, ARE YOU? THAT MUST MAKE YOU FEEL VERY BAD.
I BET YOU'RE SAD NOW, AND ALL THAT MAGIC HAS MADE YOU SO TIRED, HASN'T IT. POOR SAL. I'LL LOOK AFTER YOU.
I'LL KEEP YOU SAFE.

HEY DOC...
...OVER HERE.
WHAT YOU FOUND FRAMPTON?
ANYTHING USEFUL IN THAT BOAT?

I THINK WE'VE GOT THE MISSING GIRL HERE.
I AM NOT A MISSING GIRL.

YOU LOOK PRETTY LOST TO ME SWEETHEART.

COME ALONG, WE'LL GET YOU BACK TO PALLID ROCK.

THEY THOUGHT YOU WERE MOST LIKELY DEAD LITTLE GIRL.
AFTER WHOEVER IT WAS BROKE IN.
BROKE IN?

PRETTY BAD, THE WAY I HEARD IT. MISS CALDER'S VANISHED. ORPHANAGE WAS SUPPOSED TO BE PRETTY SECURE. NO KNOWING HOW THEY GOT IN.
OH.

I DIDN'T KNOW.

DON'T FRET ABOUT IT SWEETHEART.

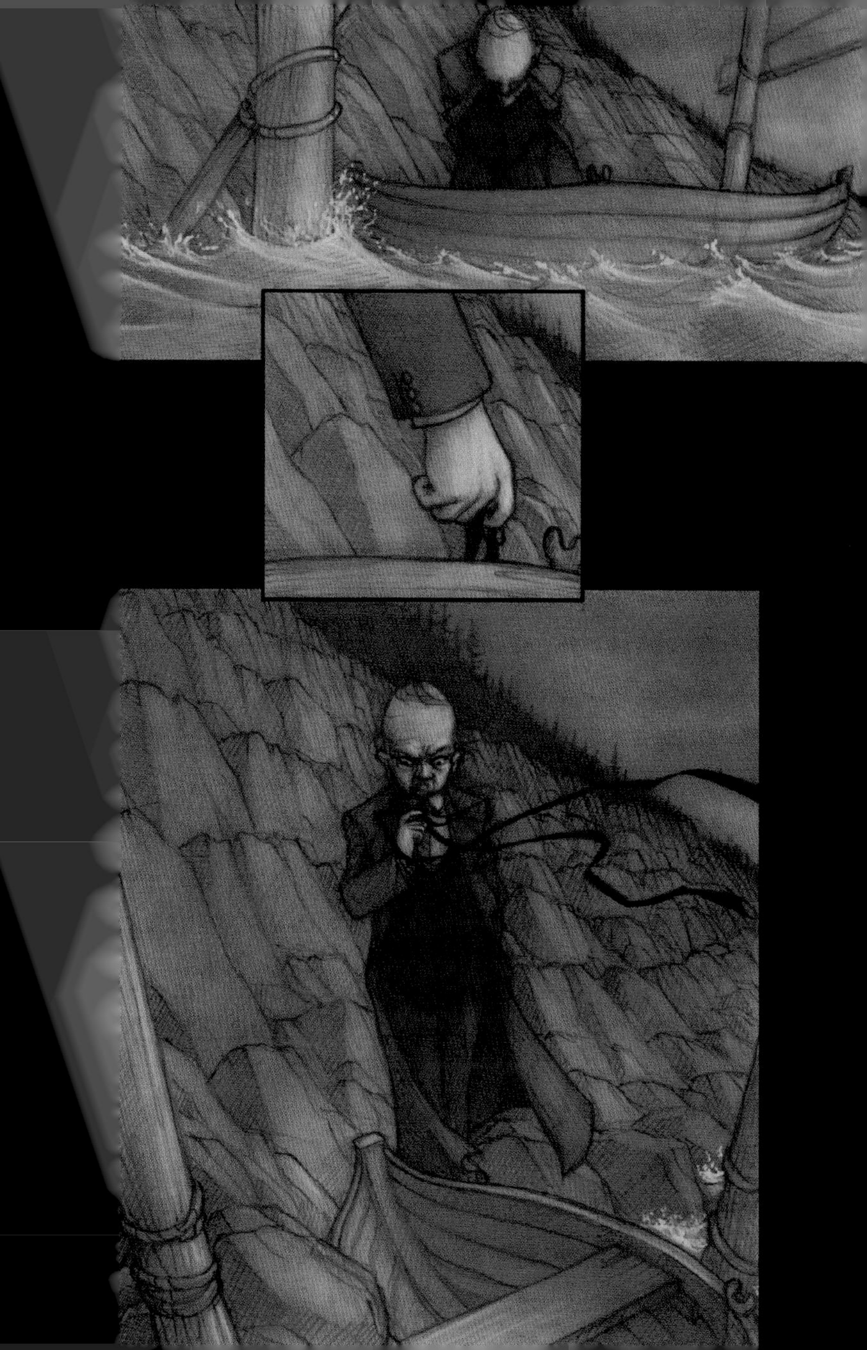

YOU HAD US ALL VERY WORRIED. I NEED YOU TO TELL ME WHAT HAPPENED.
I WAS QUITE SAFE, IT WAS OK.

DID SOMEONE TAKE YOU AWAY?
I DON'T THINK SO.

DID SOMEONE ASK YOU TO OPEN THE DOOR, OR THREATEN YOU?
NO.

THEN WHAT IN GOD'S NAME WERE YOU DOING OUTSIDE AT NIGHT?

I JUST WANTED TO GO FOR A WALK.

IN THE MIDDLE OF THE NIGHT?
WHY NOT?
BECAUSE YOU ARE A SMALL CHILD AND IT SIMPLY ISN'T SAFE FOR YOU.
I'M OK AREN'T I?
APPARENTLY. BUT MISS CALDER IS MISSING. I WONDER HOW THEY GOT IN.
WHO GOT IN?
WHOEVER TOOK MISS CALDER AWAY! UNLESS YOU THINK SHE WENT OUT FOR A LITTLE WALK TOO?
I DON'T KNOW ANYTHING.
GO TO YOUR ROOM, AND STAY THERE UNTIL TOLD OTHERWISE. UNDERSTAND? IF YOU EVER DO ANYTHING SO FOOLHARDY AGAIN YOU WILL BE IN SERIOUS TROUBLE. I WANT YOU TO THINK ABOUT WHAT YOU HAVE DONE, AND THE CONSEQUENCES OF YOUR ACTIONS.
YES SIR.

OH, HELLO.
HOW DID YOU
GET IN HERE?
THROUGH THE DOOR,
SAME AS
EVERYONE ELSE.
WAS HE
VERY CROSS
WITH YOU?
YES.
IT'S YOUR
FAULT IF SOMETHING
BAD HAS HAPPENED
TO MISS CALDER
ISN'T IT?
YOU LEFT THE
DOOR OPEN.
I DID.
AND THEY'RE ALL
SAYING SOMETHING
REALLY AWFUL
HAS HAPPENED TO HER.
MAYBE
SHE'S DEAD.

I HOPE NOT.

BUT IF SHE IS, IT'LL BE YOUR FAULT, WON'T IT?
I GUESS. I DIDN'T THINK.

EVERYONE WILL HATE YOU.
THEY DON'T LIKE ME MUCH ANYWAY.

THEY'LL REALLY HATE YOU NOW.
MAYBE THEY'LL SEND YOU AWAY, OR LOCK YOU IN A CELLAR.

I DON'T HATE YOU. I'M YOUR FRIEND.
DON'T YOU THINK I DESERVE TO BE HATED?

DID YOU MEAN HER TO GET HURT?
COURSE NOT.

SO THERE YOU GO.

WHO WERE YOU TALKING TO?
NO ONE REALLY.
HMM. COME WITH ME.

CHAPTER FOUR
I THINK IF I WAS GOING TO MAKE UP A FRIEND,
I WOULD THINK OF SOMEONE NICER THAN YOU.

IT'S GETTING DARK.
WE'LL BE HOME SAFE SOON. IT'LL BE OK.

I FEEL LIKE
I'M BEING WATCHED.

CREEPY PLACE.
WHERE DID YOU COME FROM?
I WAS JUST AROUND.

YOU DON'T HAVE TO GO TO SCHOOL.
I KNOW.

KEEP UP SALAMANDRA!

HE CAN'T SEE YOU, CAN HE?
NOPE.

COS I'M NOT REAL.
YOU'RE SO SAD AND PATHETIC THAT YOU HAD TO INVENT A FRIEND.
WHY NOT?

I THINK IF I WAS GOING TO MAKE UP A FRIEND, I'D THINK OF SOMEONE NICER THAN YOU.
NO YOU WOULDN'T, BECAUSE YOU DON'T REALLY LIKE YOURSELF EITHER.
NO ONE LIKES YOU.
NOT EVEN ME.

YOU SAID YOU DID.
I LIED...

...BUT I'M ALL YOU'VE GOT.
GO AWAY

LEAVE ME ALONE
SALAMANDRA!

COME HERE
SALAMANDRA.
WHO'S THERE?

I'M NOT SAD AND PATHETIC.
I'M NOT SAD AND PATHETIC...

FWAP
OH!

OH, LOOK AT YOU.
DID YOU FALL OUT OF YOUR NEST?

ROARK!

YOU'RE A REAL SWEETIE, AREN'T YOU?

CAN'T SEE YOUR NEST, OR YOUR PARENTS EITHER.

I GUESS YOU'RE ALL ON YOUR OWN TOO HUH?

I'LL CATCH YOU FLIES AND BUGS AND STUFF AND YOU CAN SHARE MY FOOD AND EVERYTHING.
I'LL TAKE CARE OF YOU

HEY SAL.

I SEE YOU'VE MADE SO MANY NEW FRIENDS YOU DON'T NEED ME ANY MORE.
GO AWAY. I'M NOT TALKING TO YOU.

THAT'S RIGHT.
I'VE GOT MORE FRIENDS THAN I KNOW WHAT TO DO WITH.

IF YOU SAY SORRY I'LL BE YOUR FRIEND AGAIN.
WHAT AM I SUPPOSED TO BE SORRY FOR?

EVERYTHING.
NO.

TOO BAD.

YOU JUST AREN'T AS GOOD AS YOU THINK YOU ARE.

SORRY ABOUT THAT.
IT'S OK.

YOU LOOKED LIKE YOU WERE HAVING A FIT OF SOME SORT.
YOU CAN'T SEE HER EITHER THEN?

SEE WHO?
DOESN'T MATTER.

YOU'RE REVEREND DAVIES'S SON, AREN'T YOU?

YEP.
AND YOU MUST BE SALAMANDRA
DAD'S MENTIONED YOU A FEW TIMES.
OH. WHAT'S YOUR NAME?

OWEN.

THANKS FOR RESCUING ME OWEN.
WHAT WAS GOING ON BACK THERE?

THERE'S THIS GIRL, BUT I DON'T THINK ANYONE ELSE CAN SEE HER. SHE SAYS SHE'S MY INVISIBLE FRIEND, BUT I'M NOT SO SURE. SHE PULLED MY HAIR, AND SHE KICKED ME.
THAT DOESN'T SOUND VERY FRIENDLY.

THAT'S WHAT I THOUGHT.
DOES SHE HAVE A NAME, THIS GIRL?

WELL, IF SHE GIVES YOU ANY MORE TROUBLE, JUST COME AND TELL ME.
SHE'S NEVER SAID.

THANKS. I WILL.

IF I TELL YOU A SECRET...
...WILL YOU PROMISE NOT TO TELL ANYONE, NOT EVEN YOUR DAD?
I PROMISE.

I'VE GOT A BABY CROW.
A REAL BABY CROW. I FOUND IT ON MY WINDOW, AND I FEED IT ON BUGS AND WORMS AND STUFF.
NEAT.

ONLY...
ITS GETTING BIGGER, IT'LL NEED TO FLY SOON.

WILL YOU HELP ME?
SURE.

I DO NOT THINK I WILL EVER
GET USED TO BEING DEAD.
CHAPTER FIVE

ROARK

I CAN'T MOVE.
MY LEG...

GOD HAVE MERCY ON THAT CHILD.

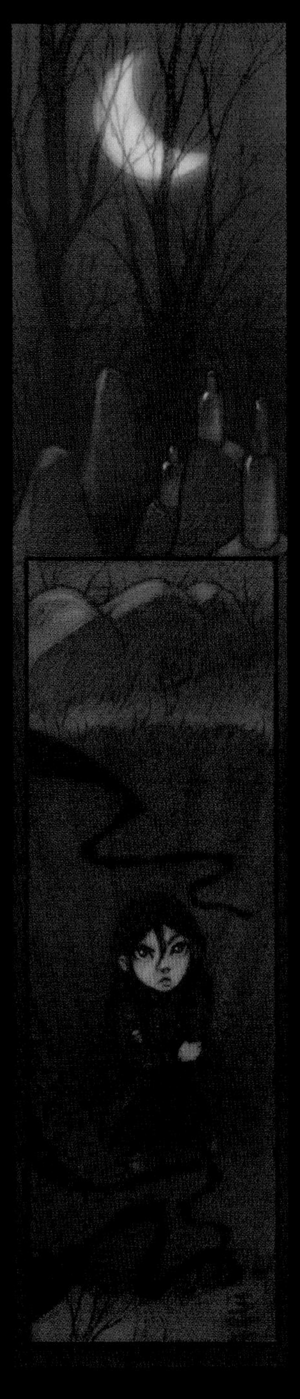

READY TO SAY SORRY YET?
NO.

I COULD HELP YOU ESCAPE.
I DON'T BELIEVE YOU.

DO YOU HAVE ANY CHOICE?
YES.

BECAUSE IT'S NOT LIKE YOU CAN USE YOUR MAGIC TO GET OUT OF HERE, IS IT? NOT WHEN YOUR ANKLE HURTS SO BADLY.
YOU HAVE TO BE ABLE TO THINK CLEARLY TO DO MAGIC, DON'T YOU?
WE'LL SEE.

POOR SALAMANDRA,
YOU LOOK SO VERY PALE AND TIRED.
MAYBE BEING OUT HERE IN THE
COLD ALL NIGHT WILL KILL YOU.
MAYBE WILD ANIMALS WILL
EAT YOU UP, OR WORSE.
WHAT DO
YOU THINK?
YOU AREN'T HELPING.
YOU KNOW THAT,
DON'T YOU?

AREN'T I?
WHAT'S SHE
DOING HERE?
WHO ARE YOU
SWEETHEART?

OF COURSE I CAN PET.
YOU CAN SEE ME?
OH, THERE'S NOTHING I CAN DO.
I DON'T THINK I'M EVER GOING TO GET USED TO BEING DEAD

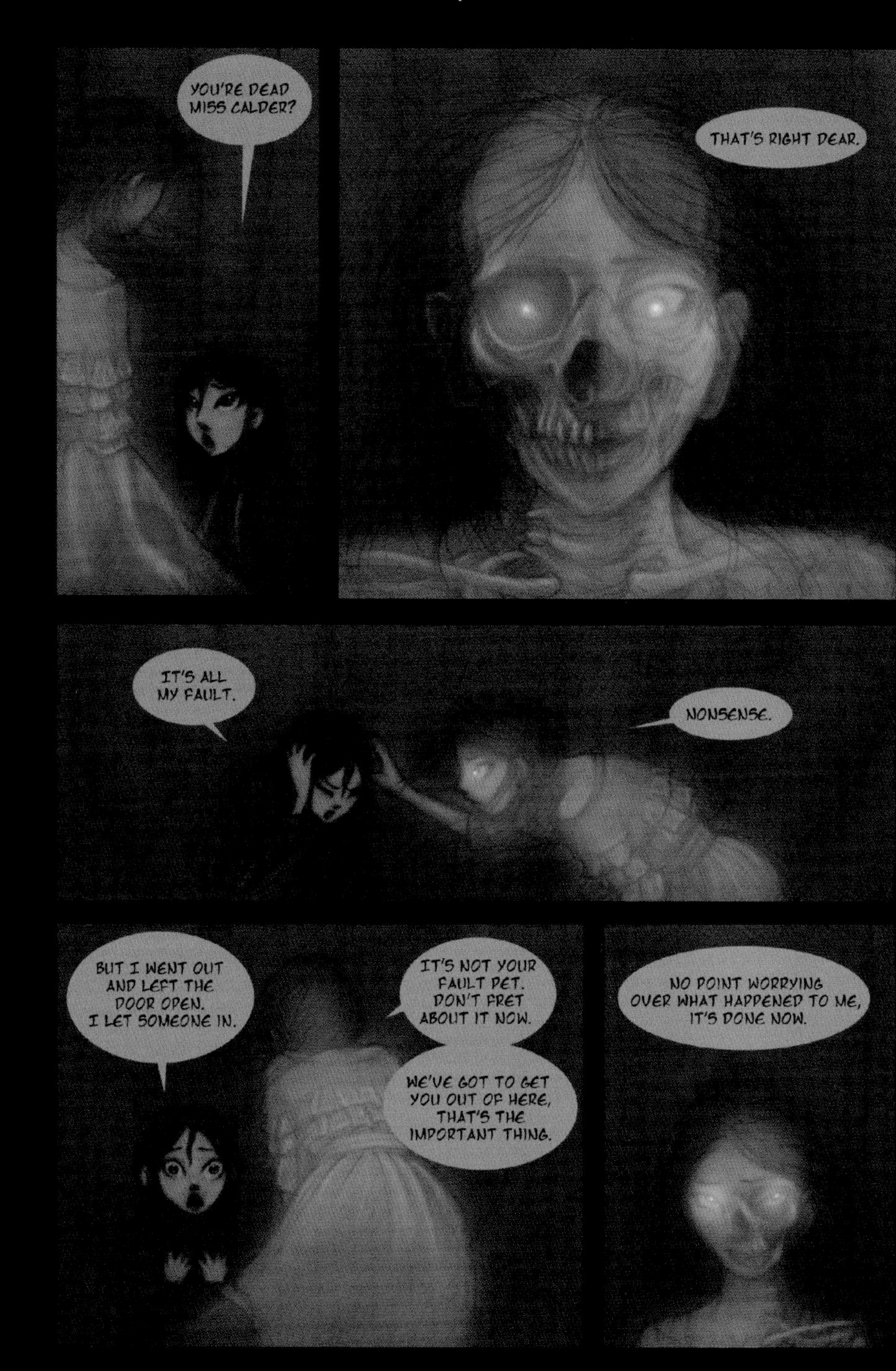
YOU'RE DEAD MISS CALDER?
THAT'S RIGHT DEAR.
IT'S ALL MY FAULT.
NONSENSE.
BUT I WENT OUT AND LEFT THE DOOR OPEN. I LET SOMEONE IN.
IT'S NOT YOUR FAULT PET. DON'T FRET ABOUT IT NOW.
WE'VE GOT TO GET YOU OUT OF HERE, THAT'S THE IMPORTANT THING.
NO POINT WORRYING OVER WHAT HAPPENED TO ME, IT'S DONE NOW.

BUT YOU'RE DEAD!
HAPPENS TO ALL OF US IN THE END. NOW, DO YOU THINK YOUR LITTLE FRIEND COULD HELP LIFT YOU?
PROBABLY NOT. ANYWAY, SHE'S NOT MY FRIEND.
WHERE'S SHE GONE?
NEVER MIND. I'LL HAVE TO FETCH HELP.
THANK YOU.
YOU BE BRAVE...
...AND I'LL BE BACK WITH HELP REAL SOON.

NOW...
...WHAT CAN YOU TELL ME ...
...ABOUT YOUR PARENTS?
THEY'RE PRETTY WEIRD AND I HAVEN'T SEEN THEM IN AGES.
YOU SAID YOUR FATHER CONJURE DEMONS. HOW DOES HE DO THAT?
HOW WOULD I KNOW?

I THINK YOU'RE GOING TO HAVE TO TRY HARDER
IF YOU GIVE ME THE RIGHT ANSWERS, WE CAN BE FRIENDS AGAIN ...
... AND YOU WANT US TO BE FRIENDS, DON'T YOU?
YOU DON'T WANT TO BE MY ENEMY SALAMANDRA.
REALLY YOU DON'T.
I COULD DO THIS TO YOU.
I'M MUCH STRONGER THAN I LOOK.
ARE YOU GOING TO TELL ME HOW HE SUMMONS DEMONS?
I DON'T KNOW.

I DON'T KNOW.
I REALLY DON'T KNOW ANYTHING.
RRRIP
I WANT TO KNOW EVERYTHING ABOUT YOUR MAGIC. EVERYTHING.
SALAMANDRA? WHERE ARE YOU CHILD?

Chapter Six

Do You Think People Who Do Magic Are Bad?

WHAT HAPPENED TO YOUR BEAR?
HI OWEN.
HE WAS TORTURED.

THAT SOUNDS BAD.
YEAH.

I FOUND YOUR CROW.

I'M SORRY I DIDN'T GET CHANCE TO TELL YOU BEFORE.

IT MIGHT BE READY TO FLY. I COULD FETCH IT DOWN FROM MY ROOM.
THAT'S OK. AND THANKS.
THANKS.
IT'S GOT ALL ITS FEATHERS NOW
ROARK.
HI THERE. DID YOU MISS ME?
ROARK!
I GUESS SO.
I DON'T THINK IT CAN UNDERSTAND ME REALLY, BUT IT'S NICE TO TALK TO.
SO LONG CROW.

I WONDER WHAT'S GOT INTO HIM?
STOP IT!
JUST STOP IT!

HMM...
COME ON, SHOW YOURSELF.
WHERE ARE YOU?

WHO WERE YOU TALKING TO?
NO ONE REALLY.

A LITTLE GIRL BY ANY CHANCE?
PRETTY? BIG EYES?
YOU CAN SEE HER? BUT SHE'S MY INVISIBLE FRIEND.
I BET SHE TOLD YOU THAT.
YEAH.
DON'T LISTEN TO HER. SHE'S NOT YOUR FRIEND.
SHE'S THE ONLY FRIEND I'VE GOT.
THAT'S NOT TRUE.
HERE,
YOU CAN HAVE MY BEAR.
HE CAN BE YOUR FRIEND.
HE'S BEEN THROUGH SOME PRETTY BAD STUFF SO YOU'VE GOT TO PROMISE TO BE NICE TO HIM AND LOOK AFTER HIM REALLY WELL.
I PROMISE.

NO CROW, NO BEAR, NO INVISIBLE FRIEND WHO HATES ME.
I'VE HAD BETTER DAYS.
WOULD YOU LIKE TO SEE MY TREE?
OK.
I SIT UP HERE WHEN I WANT TO THINK.

IT SEEMS LIKE A GOOD THINKING PLACE.
I DON'T MIND IF YOU WANT TO COME HERE TOO.
ROARK!
I THOUGHT YOU'D GONE OFF TO DO CROW THINGS.
WELL, WE ARE SITTING IN A TREE.
I THOUGHT WE WERE FRIENDS ALREADY.
YOUR TREE, MY CROW... I THINK THIS COULD WORK.
WE COULD BE FRIENDS.

OTHER PEOPLE HAVE SAID THAT AND THEY DIDN'T MEAN IT, SO I WASN'T SURE.
ARE WE TALKING ABOUT THE INVISIBLE GIRL HERE?
YER
WHAT IS SHE ANYWAY?
THERE'S SOMETHING NOT RIGHT THERE.
I DON'T KNOW. NOTHING GOOD. I THOUGHT IT WAS JUST ME, BUT SEEING THAT BOY...
DO YOU KNOW ANNAMARIE NIGHTSHADE?
I'VE HEARD HER NAME.
DAD REALLY DOESN'T LIKE HER.
DO YOU KNOW WHERE SHE LIVES?
NO.

SHE'S THE ONLY PERSON I KNOW WHO MIGHT BE ABLE TO HELP WELL, REALLY SPEAKING SHE'S THE ONLY PERSON I KNOW OUTSIDE THIS PLACE.
WHAT ABOUT YOUR PARENTS?
I DON'T THINK THEY COUNT. AND THEY WOULDN'T HELP.
WE COULD GO TOMORROW, AFTER CHURCH. NO ONE WOULD NOTICE.
DO YOU HAVE ANY IDEA WHERE SHE LIVES?
IT WAS FOGGY.
I WAS ON A BROOM. DUH.
OK, FORGET I ASKED.

NO?
DO YOU KNOW WHERE SHE IS?
SO WE DO THIS MY WAY.
WE'VE JUST GONE ROUND IN A BIG CIRCLE.
I HAD TO FIGURE THINGS OUT. I CAN'T REMEMBER, BUT THIS FEELS RIGHT.
AND NOW?
WE GO THIS WAY.
HOW DO YOU KNOW?
I JUST DO.
IT'S LIKE HOW YOU TELL WHICH WAY IS UP.
YOU CAN TELL WHICH WAY IS UP, CAN'T YOU OWEN?
WHAT DO YOU THINK?

WHAT IS THAT?
THEY'RE OLD TRAPS, I HEARD.
DON'T KNOW. GUESS THEY ALL GOT CAUGHT.
WHAT WOULD YOU CATCH IN THEM?
I'M PRETTY SURE WE'RE GOING THE WRONG WAY.

HE SAYS WITCHES ARE EVIL.
HMM. I THINK I CAN SEE WHY DAD DOESN'T LIKE HER.
ANNAMARIE NIGHTSHADE
I DON'T THINK ANNAMARIE IS EVIL. SHE GAVE ME BROWNIES AND EVERYTHING
DO YOU THINK PEOPLE WHO DO MAGIC ARE BAD?
WELL, THAT'S ALL RIGHT THEN.
I DON'T KNOW. I'D NEVER REALLY THOUGHT ABOUT IT.
YOU MIGHT WANT TO THINK ABOUT IT.
DOESN'T SEEM SO BAD TO ME.

YOU WEREN'T SUPPOSED TO BE ABLE TO DO THAT.
I'VE GOT A BIT OF A PROBLEM.
WE CAN SIT OUT HERE ON THE GRASS...
...AND I'LL FETCH US SOME DRINKS.
I DON'T THINK SHE WANTS ME IN THE HOUSE. PROBABLY BECAUSE I SET FIRE TO HER CHAIR LAST TIME.
SOUNDS TO ME LIKE WHAT YOU'VE GOT IS SOME KIND OF MALEVOLENT SPIRIT. MIGHT WELL BE THE SORT THAT FEEDS ON OTHER PEOPLE'S SUFFERING.

SO HOW DO I MAKE HER GO AWAY?
DO YOU KNOW HER TRUE NAME?
NO.
UNHELPFUL. ALTHOUGH...
I HAVE A BOX YOU CAN USE.
IS IT A MAGIC BOX?
NO, IT'S AN OLD JEWELLERY BOX OF MY MOTHERS...
...BUT IT HAS A LOCK AND A KEY, THAT'S THE MAIN THING.
WHAT DO I HAVE TO DO?
SHE HAS TO GO INTO THE BOX. THEN YOU LOCK IT SHUT, BURY THE BOX AND PLANT A TREE OVER IT. KEEP THE KEY.
GREAT, THANKS.

I AM NOT A WITCH · I AM

A · · SOMETHING ELSE ·

CHAPTER SEVEN

JUST ONE QUESTION. HOW DO WE GET HER IN THE BOX?

I'M WORKING ON THAT.

HI.
HELLO.
HOW'S IT GOING?
PRETTY GOOD.
SEEN ANYTHING MORE OF YOUR INVISIBLE FRIEND LATELY?
NO, NOT FOR AGES.
WELL, I GUESS THAT'S GOOD.
SHE'S MOVED ON.
MAYBE SHE'S GONE.
I DON'T THINK SO. WE'LL JUST HAVE TO KEEP OUR EYES OPEN.
WHAT ARE WE LOOKING FOR?
SOMEONE UNHAPPY, TALKING TO THEMSELVES.

THAT COULD BE ALMOST ANYONE. NO ONE'S REALLY HAPPY HERE.
NOT EVEN YOU?

RAGGED ISLE
GO AND TALK TO HER.
I DON'T KNOW WHAT TO SAY.
SHE'S A GIRL.

YOU TALK TO ME OK OWEN.
YOU'RE... WELL.
YOU'RE DIFFERENT.
OH, THANK YOU VERY MUCH.
HI, YOU'RE ?UH ? JOSEPHINE, RIGHT?
MM.
OK, THAT'S GOOD.
THIS IS HOPELESS.
WE'RE LOOKING FOR A GIRL WHO SAYS SHE'S YOUR INVISIBLE FRIEND BUT IS REALLY MEAN. HAVE YOU SEEN HER?
NO.
SEE?

I THINK IT'S HER.
SHE SAID NO.
SHE WAS LYING.
NOW WHAT?
WE KEEP AN EYE ON HER.

WHO THREW THAT?
JOSEPHINE DAY!
HERE! NOW!

IT WASN'T HER.
THEN WHO WAS IT, EH?
IT WAS ME.

WHY DID YOU DO THAT?
DO WHAT?
SAY IT WAS YOU WHEN IT WASN'T.
COS I KNEW THE GIRL WHO REALLY DID IT WOULDN'T SAY SO.
SHE SAID YOU'D BE MEAN TO ME IF I WAS NICE TO YOU.
SHE SAID YOU'D PUT A SPELL ON ME AND TURN ME INTO A FROG OR SOMETHING.
WHAT DO YOU THINK?
I'M SCARED OF HER.
I DON'T KNOW WHAT TO DO.

THANKS.
NEARLY DONE NOW.

I REALLY AM SORRY.

VERY SORRY.
YES...
I'LL DO WHATEVER YOU SAY.

NOW!

WHAT ARE YOU DOING?
JOSEPHINE, HELP ME, SHE'S GOING TO KILL ME!
GO INSIDE JOSEPHINE, YOU DON'T HAVE TO STAY HERE.
WHAT ARE YOU GOING TO DO TO HER SALAMANDRA?
MAKE SURE SHE CAN'T HURT ANYONE ELSE.

PLEASE JOSEPHINE!
HAVEN'T I ALWAYS BEEN YOUR FRIEND?
AREN'T I THE ONLY ONE WHO'S NICE TO YOU?
DON'T LET HER HURT ME.
DON'T HURT HER,
SHE'S JUST A LITTLE GIRL.
SHE'S NOT JUST A LITTLE GIRL, SHE'S SOMETHING VERY NASTY.
THANK YOU OWEN.
IN YOU GO.
NO! PLEASE NO, NOT IN THERE.
YES, IN THERE.

I WOULDN'T HURT ANYONE, BUT SHE'S A WITCH!
WON'T ONE OF YOU STOP HER??
I'M NOT A WITCH I'M A... A...
... SOMETHING ELSE.
NOW GET IN THE BOX BEFORE I REALLY GET CROSS.

SOMETIMES THE DEMON IS ONLY AS BIG AS YOU THINK IT IS...
...ESPECIALLY IF YOU HAPPEN TO BE SALAMANDRA.
WHAT IS IT?
NOT SURE.
SLAM
CLICK
WE SHOULDN'T HAVE ANY MORE TROUBLE WITH IT NOW.

DO YOU THINK THAT'S IT THEN? HAS SHE GONE?
MAYBE, FOR NOW.

THANKS FOR HELPING OWEN.
ANY TIME. IT WAS... FUN I GUESS.

WE COULD GO SIT IN YOUR TREE.

YEAH. THAT WOULD BE GOOD.

I DID A GOOD THING?
I'D SAY.
I KNOW WHAT YOU'RE THINKING.
REALLY? EVEN THE BIT WHERE I COVER YOU IN MUD?
IT'S NOT WHERE YOU CAME FROM THAT MATTERS.
IT'S WHO I CHOOSE TO BE. I KNOW.
I'M STILL GOING TO COVER YOU IN MUD THOUGH.

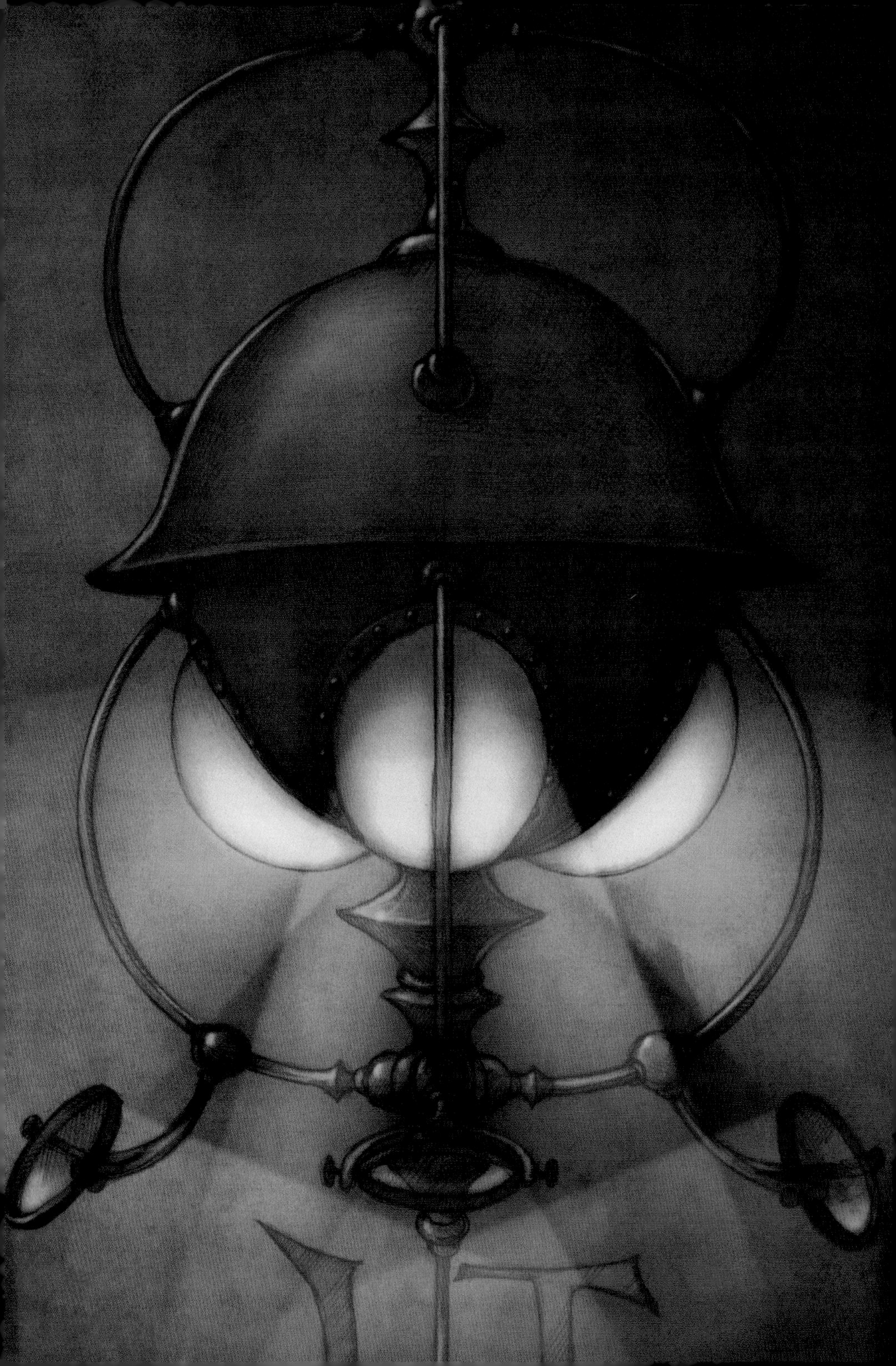

HOPELESS MAINE
BOOK TWO

INHERITANCE

TOM AND NIMUE BROWN

CHAPTER ONE
HAPPY
FOUNDERS
DAY
I'D THROW MYSELF INTO THE SEA

HAPPY FOUNDERS DAY OWEN.
LOOKING FORWARD TO THE FOUNDERS DAY FEAST SALAMANDRA?
WHY IS NONE OF IT EDIBLE?
THIS IS WHAT THE FOUNDING FATHERS FOUND WHEN THEY GOT HERE.
WHY DID THEY STAY?
I'D HAVE THROWN MYSELF IN THE SEA.
DEFINITELY.

JED GRIMES GENERAL STORE
ANOTHER MERMAID SIGHTING MISTER JONES?
BAKERS
IT WAS THE CHEERIEST STORY I COULD FIND.
THE HOPELESS VENDETTA
OH?
DEAD PEOPLE ARE WEARYING AFTER A WHILE.
GRAVELY DISAPPOINTING.
HEY, THAT WAS ALMOST FUNNY!
WHAP!

WHAT IS IT MRS DAVIES?
I WANT TO TALK ABOUT YOU.
I'M DOING OK.
GOOD, BUT WE SHOULD THINK ABOUT YOUR FUTURE, IF YOU HAVE ANY SURVIVING FAMILY.
IF I TELL YOU WHO MY PARENTS ARE, WILL YOU MAKE ME GO BACK TO THEM?
NO. BUT YOU MIGHT HAVE OTHER FAMILY.
I DON'T THINK SO.

PLEASE, TRUST ME.
TELL ME WHO YOU ARE.
I HATE THEM!
NOW YOU'RE OLDER, YOU MIGHT FIND A NEW HOME, WITH RELATIVES.
DUROSIMI AND MELISANDRA O'STOAT.
I DON'T EVER WANT TO SEE THEM AGAIN.
UNLESS THEY WERE BEING EATEN BY SEA MONSTERS OR SOMETHING.

NO ONE'S SEEN THEM IN A LONG TIME.
YOU PROBABLY ARE AN ORPHAN.
GOOD.
BUT YOU HAVE A GRANDFATHER, BALTHAZAR LEMON. HE'S A VERY SWEET OLD MAN.
HE IS?
HE'S AN INVENTOR AND HE LIVES IN THE LIGHTHOUSE.
SO I COULD LIVE WITH HIM?
IT'S A POSSIBILITY.

I DON'T FEEL ANY DIFFERENT.
I'VE NOT CHANGED YOU, THAT'S WHY. JUST HOW YOU LOOK.
HOW LONG CAN I STAY LIKE THIS?
AS LONG AS I KEEP CONCENTRATING...
...WHICH IS WHY I DON'T DO THAT ALL THE TIME.

IF YOU WERE AN ORPHAN, YOU'D BE LEAVING US THIS SUMMER.
WHAT'S THAT SUPPOSED TO MEAN?
ONLY THAT WE SHOULD THINK ABOUT THE FUTURE.
I'D ASSUMED IT WOULD BE A LOT LIKE THIS.
YOU SHOULD DO SOMETHING USEFUL WITH YOURSELF
CLONK!

IT'LL BE FUN OWEN, PROMISE.
BUT A CRAZY MAN LIVES OUT THERE.
THAT CRAZY MAN MIGHT BE MY GRANDFATHER.
WON'T YOU COME WITH ME, PLEASE?

WHAT ARE YOU LOOKING FOR, FRAMPTON?
ANYTHING.
AREN'T THERE ENOUGH DEAD PEOPLE TO MAKE NEWS OUT OF?
DEATH ISN'T NEWS.
DEPENDS ON HOW IT COMES, DOESN'T IT?
I HEAR YOU ANNAMARIE.
SO DO SOMETHING ABOUT IT.

Chapter Two

"She said she'd come back, but she never did."

HAVE YOU SEEN HER?
SEEN WHO MR LEMON?

GONE.
MIGHT BE COMING BACK.
WHO'S GONE?
WHEN THE MOON WAS FULL, SHE SAILED OUT ALONG THE LIGHT AND WE NEVER SAW HER AGAIN.

SHE SAID SHE'D COME BACK, BUT SHE NEVER DID.
BUT YOU HAVE COME BACK. YOU LOOK SO MUCH YOUNGER.
MY NAME IS SALAMANDRA.
I DON'T KNOW YOU. BUT YOU LOOK LIKE MY DAUGHTER.
MELISANDRA WAS MY MOTHER. IS SHE YOUR DAUGHTER?
I HAVE NO DAUGHTER.
NOT ANY MORE.
ALL GONE.
WE SHOULD BE GETTING BACK NOW, BEFORE IT GETS DARK.

HE'S MAD.
HE MIGHT BE ALL I'VE GOT.
HE SEEMED NICE THOUGH. YOUR MOTHER TOLD ME ABOUT HIM. HE BUILT THE LIGHTHOUSE.
AT LEAST OUR BOY'S AT PEACE NOW, DOCTOR.

I THOUGHT YOU HATED THEM.
I DO.
THAT'S WHY I'M REALLY HOPING THEY'RE IN HERE.

IS IT ME, OR
IS IT VERY QUIET?
EXTREMELY SO.
MRS WITHERSPOON,
WHAT'S HAPPENED?

YOUR MOTHER'S HAD A BIT OF A TURN.
YOUR FATHER AND DOCTOR WILLOUGHBY
ARE WITH HER. YOU'D BEST WAIT HERE.

WELL, THANK YOU FOR YOUR TIME DOCTOR.
I WISH I COULD DO MORE, TRULY I DO.
SO SHE'LL GET BETTER, RIGHT?
I HOPE SO.
SHE'S NOT THE FIRST CASE, NOT THAT ANYONE'S DIED YET. MIND YOU, THERE'S ALWAYS A FIRST, ISN'T THERE?
THANK YOU DOCTOR WILLOUGHBY.
AND SHE ALWAYS WAS DELICATE.
I WOULDN'T WANT TO KEEP YOU FROM YOUR OTHER PATIENTS.

DON'T HESITATE TO CALL FOR ME WHEN SHE GETS WORSE.

MUM'S GOING TO DIE, ISN'T SHE?

YOU MUSTN'T EVER SAY THAT, OR THINK THAT, EVER AGAIN.

Chapter Three

"The Scrying Not the Newt Peeling"

THERE MUST BE SOMETHING YOU CAN DO.
I'VE NEVER TRIED TO MAKE ANYONE BETTER. I DON'T KNOW HOW TO DO IT.
BUT YOU DO MAGIC.
A BIT, YES, BUT I DO HAVE LIMITS. I DON'T EVEN KNOW WHAT'S WRONG WITH HER, SO HOW CAN I FIX THINGS?
I'M SORRY, I SHOULDN'T HAVE ASKED. I JUST DON'T KNOW WHAT ELSE TO DO.
WE SHOULD ASK ANNAMARIE. SHE IS A WITCH AFTER ALL. SHE MIGHT HAVE SOME IDEAS.

NO.
GO AWAY.
I KNOW WHAT YOU WANT, AND I CAN'T DO IT.
BUT WE HADN'T EVEN ASKED YET.
WHY NOT?
BECAUSE I'D NEED HER PERMISSION.
BUT I HAVEN'T ASKED HER EITHER.
NO POINT MY DUMPLING. SHE'LL SAY NO.

HOW DO YOU KNOW?
CRYSTAL BALL PRECIOUS.
NOW, IF YOU DON'T MIND, I HAVE SOME NEWTS TO PEEL.
WOULD YOU TEACH ME HOW TO DO THAT?
MAYBE. NOT RIGHT NOW THOUGH.
THE SCRYING, NOT THE NEWT PEELING!

THERE'S A WHOLE WORLD OUT THERE.
YOUR GRANDMOTHER COULDN'T BEAR BEING AWAY FROM IT.
DID SHE REALLY LEAVE?
OH YES. BUT I HAD TO MAKE THE LIGHT FOR HER. I HAD TO STAY BEHIND.
DO YOU MISS HER?
EVERY DAY.
WAS SHE REALLY A PRINCESS?
OH YES.

AND ARE YOU A PRINCE?
NO, I WAS SHIP'S COOK. I SAVED HER FROM THE SEA. I LOVED HER AND SHE WAS LONELY, FELT SORRY FOR ME.
THAT'S ALL A LONG TIME AGO.
THEN I MADE THE LIGHTHOUSE. NOW I AM A LIGHTHOUSE KEEPER, BUT THERE ARE NEVER ANY SHIPS.
DON'T YOU THINK THAT'S ODD? NO SHIPS AT ALL.
CAN I SEE INSIDE THE LIGHTHOUSE?
YOUR WISH IS MY COMMAND LITTLE ONE.

WHEN I GO, ALL THIS WILL BE YOURS.
YOU'RE NOT GOING ANY TIME SOON ARE YOU?
WHO KNOWS?
CAN I COME AND LIVE WITH YOU? I HATE THE ORPHANAGE.
YOU CAN VISIT.
I LIED! AND YOU PAY FAR TOO MUCH ATTENTION TO WHAT I SAY.
NGARGH...!
WHAT HAPPENED TO MY WISH BEING YOUR COMMAND?
SO SHOULD I IGNORE WHAT YOU SAID JUST NOW AND MOVE IN ANYWAY?

I JUST WANT TO HELP!
I KNOW YOU DO, DEAR ONE.

THEN WHY...?
PLEASE. DON'T MAKE THIS HARDER FOR ME THAN IT ALREADY IS.

I'M SORRY.

Chapter Four

"It'll be really undignified, Promise"

... IS THE ONLY WAY.
WE MUST MAKE SOME SACRIFICES.
ICA'S LAST YEAR'S CLOTHES
IN THIS YEAR'S STYLE

SORRY ABOUT THIS.
IT'S NOT YOUR FAULT. I DID SKIP SCHOOL AGAIN.
DAD'S NOT IN A GOOD MOOD RIGHT NOW.
I NOTICED.
HOW IS YOUR MOTHER DOING?
MUCH THE SAME. STILL IN BED.
IT DOES STINK DOWN HERE.
AND WE GET TO CLEAN UP.
WONDERFUL.

SO WHAT DID YOU DO TO GET THIS JOB?
ANSWERED HIM BACK ONCE TOO OFTEN.
WHAT DO YOU THINK COULD MAKE A SMELL THAT BAD?
THAT MAYBE?
OK, THAT'S PRETTY HORRIBLE.
SHALL I JUST BURN IT?
BE MY GUEST.

WE SHOULD STAY HERE FOR A BIT. I DON'T THINK YOUR DAD WOULD APPROVE OF THE CLEANING METHOD.
HE DOESN'T APPROVE OF ANYTHING MUCH.
DID YOU ASK YOUR MOTHER ABOUT ANNAMARIE?
YES.
AND?
NO.
NOW WHAT?
NO IDEA.

SPLAT
SPLAT
SPLAT
SPLAT
WEIRDOS!
BEEN CALLED WORSE !
SPLAT
OK,
HE ASKED FOR IT.

I NEED YOU TO FETCH DOCTOR WILLOUGHBY AGAIN.
HE'S MAKING HER WORSE.
HE IS THE ONLY HOPE YOUR MOTHER HAS.
I WON'T DO IT. HE'S EVIL.
CELLARS.
RIGHT NOW.

THAT'S IT. PRESS THE PASTRY INTO THE DISH.
NOW, TAKE YOUR OTHER INGREDIENTS,
AND CUT THEM UP AS SMALL AS YOU CAN
SO NO ONE CAN TELL WHAT THEY ARE.
ABIGAIL?...
YES, YOU CAN TAKE THE EYE OUT.
SALAMANDRA...
WHAT HAVE YOU DONE NOW?
SORRY.
IT SLIPPED.
GO AND CLEAN UP.

GO AWAY.
YOU CAN"T STAY UP THERE ALL DAY.
I'M NOT GOING ANYWHERE UNTIL YOU COME DOWN.
SUIT YOURSELF.
YOU KNOW, A LOT OF KIDS HERE DON'T REMEMBER THEIR MOTHERS. SOME OF US DIDN'T HAVE VERY NICE ONES TO BEGIN WITH. YOUR MOTHER... EVERYONE LOVES HER AND SHE'S VERY SPECIAL.
AND NOW SHE'S GONE AND THERE ISN'T A SINGLE THING I CAN DO ABOUT IT.
OWEN...
I THINK THAT'S HOW IT GOES SOMETIMES.

I THINK IT'S THE DOC'S FAULT. HE MADE HER WORSE, NOT BETTER.
ARE YOU SURE?
YES, AND I COULDN'T DO ANYTHING AND ANNAMARIE WOULDN'T HELP AND...
PLEASE COME DOWN OWEN OR I'LL HAVE TO MAKE YOU.
YOU WOULDN'T!!?
TRY ME.
IT'LL BE REALLY UNDIGNIFIED PROMISE.

SHE WAS SO KIND TO ME. I'M GOING TO MISS HER TOO. EVERYONE IS, AND I KNOW IT'S GOT TO BE WORSE FOR YOU, BUT YOU AREN'T ON YOUR OWN.
I'VE GOT TO GET OUT OF HERE.
THE ORPHANAGE? MAYBE WE COULD BOTH RUN AWAY AND LIVE WITH MY GRANDFATHER.
NOT JUST THE ORPHANAGE, THE WHOLE ISLAND.
YOU KNOW, THERE'S A WHOLE WORLD OUT THERE AND I WANT TO SEE IT. THE TROUBLE IS, NO ONE EVER LEAVES THIS PLACE.
MY GRANDMOTHER LEFT.
SHE DID?
MY GRANDFATHER TOLD ME.
SAL, HE'S TOTALLY MAD.
YES, BUT THAT DOESN'T MEAN HE HAS TO BE WRONG ABOUT EVERYTHING.

CHAPTER FIVE
"WE ARE NO MORE THAN CLAY"

THERE IS A WAY.
IF YOU REALLY, REALLY WANT TO GO, THEN I'LL HELP YOU. I WANT TO GO WITH YOU.
I DON'T KNOW IF I'D BE ABLE TO LOOK AFTER YOU.
I THINK I CAN LOOK AFTER MYSELF PRETTY WELL.
OK, LET'S TALK TO YOUR GRANDFATHER THEN.
BOTH OF US, TOGETHER.
IT'S A PLAN.

WE ARE NO MORE THAN CLAY.

WHAT SHALL WE DO TODAY THEN, FATHER?
I THOUGHT MAYBE I'D DIG A FEW MORE GRAVES, JUST IN CASE.
OR SET UP AN ALTAR TO DARK AND TERRIBLE GODS.
SET FIRE TO THE KITCHEN MAYBE.
YES?

NGRRR...
JUST IN TIME TO HELP ME COOK IT!
YOU'RE GOING TO EAT THAT?
I'M NOT GOING TO DANCE THE TANGO WITH IT.
COME ON, MAKE YOURSELVES USEFUL.

YOU SAID GRANDMOTHER ESCAPED FROM THE ISLAND.
WE WANT TO ESCAPE TOO.
COULD YOU TELL US HOW TO DO IT?
NO.
PLEASE...
THEN YOU'LL BE GONE AS WELL,
AND I'LL HAVE NO HOPE OF FINDING HER AGAIN.

IT WAS AN IDEA.
I'LL WORK ON HIM.
THANKS.
WHY DON'T WE GO TO THE BRIDGE OF BOTTLES, SEE IF ANYTHING NEW'S BEEN LEFT?
NOT IN THE MOOD.
BEACHCOMBING?
NAH.

I'M DONE.
MAKE THAT TWO OF US JOSEPHINE.

ANOTHER ONE.
LOOKS THAT WAY.

Chapter Six

"Maybe I'll be able to come back one day

PLEASE.
OWEN REALLY NEEDS TO GET AWAY FROM HERE.
IT TAKES ONE TO MAN THE LIGHT.
I WON'T DO IT AGAIN.
THAT'S WHY YOU COULDN'T LEAVE WHEN SHE DID.
YES.
BROKE MY HEART.
OK, WHAT IF I STAY.
WHAT IF YOU SHOW ME HOW TO MAKE THE LIGHT SO YOU AND OWEN CAN ESCAPE?
YOU'D DO THAT?
YES.
WE NEED A FULL MOON.
THAT'S THREE DAYS AWAY.
MEET ME HERE AT DUSK, BRING WHATEVER YOU NEED.

YOU SEEMED SO CERTAIN THAT YOU WANTED TO GO.
I CAN'T, NOT IF YOU'RE GOING TO. THAT'S WHAT GRANDFATHER SAID.
I CAN'T BEAR TO BE HERE. I FEEL SO CLOSED IN. I NEED TO GET OUT THERE AND DO SOMETHING.
DO WHAT?
I DON'T REALLY KNOW. I WANT TO TRAVEL. LEARN. UNDERSTAND. THE REST OF THE WORLD CAN'T BE LIKE THIS.
WHAT IF IT IS?
CHEER ME UP WHY DON'T YOU?
I DO WHAT I CAN.

MAYBE I'LL BE ABLE TO COME BACK ONE DAY AND MAKE THINGS BETTER HERE.
THAT'S A GOOD THOUGHT. YOU DO WHAT YOU NEED TO DO OWEN.
ARE YOU SURE YOU'LL BE OK?
I'LL BE FINE. DON'T WORRY ABOUT ME.

BLACK SWAN BAKERY
THANKS!
WELL... YOU KNOW...
MY DAD'S HAD TO BURY A COUPLE OF PEOPLE THIS WEEK.
WELL, IT'S MORE ME WHO DOES THE DIGGING, HE JUST DOES THE SPIRIT BIT.
THAT'S NOT GOOD.

I THINK DOC WILLOUGHBY IS KILLING PEOPLE.
WHY WOULD HE DO THAT?
I DON'T KNOW.
NO.
NOT MY PROBLEM ANYMORE.
YOU SHOULD TELL SOMEONE.
NO ONE BELIEVES ME.
I BELIEVE YOU.

I'D FORGOTTEN WHAT IT'S LIKE, BEING ALL BY MYSELF.
ROARK!
I KNOW I'VE STILL GOT YOU, BUT YOU'RE NOT MUCH OF A CONVERSATIONALIST.
MIND YOU, NEITHER'S OWEN, SOMETIMES.

SO THIS IS IT THEN?
I'LL COME BACK. I PROMISE.
I'LL MISS YOU OWEN.
I'LL MISS YOU TOO SAL.
READY??!

FOR A MOMENT, SHE THINKS ABOUT NOT DOING THIS...

AAAAAAAAAAAAAAAAAAAAAAAAAAAAAAAAAAAAAAAAAAAAAAAAAA

Chapter Seven
"And I'm pretty sure lunch had blood in it."

WHERE IS OWEN??
HE LEFT THE ISLAND.
BUT THAT'S NOT POSSIBLE!
HE TOOK A LITTLE BOAT AND ROWED AWAY.
WHAT HAVE YOU DONE TO HIM?
WHAT? OWEN'S MY FRIEND! I WOULDN'T DO ANYTHING TO HARM HIM.
NO. GO BACK TO YOUR DORMITORY SALAMANDRA.
GO.

HOW LONG DO YOU THINK HE'LL BE GONE CROWS? A MONTH? A YEAR? LONGER?
ROARK.
I MISS HIM. I HOPE HE'S OK.
I DON'T THINK MY GRANDFATHER'S COMING BACK. IT'S MISERABLE WITHOUT THEM.
INTERESTING LOOKING BOOKS. AND THIS JUST NEEDS A CLEAN.
WHAT DO YOU THINK CROWS?

IS IT TRUE YOUNG OWEN'S LEFT US?
YEP.
USUALLY THEY COME BACK, IN MY EXPERIENCE.
I THINK HE'S REALLY GONE, MR JONES.
WOULD YOU LIKE A NEWS SHEET?
DOES IT HAVE ANYTHING GOOD IN IT?
THREE DEATHS, TWO DISAPPEARANCES AND A UNICORN TURKEY.
I'LL PASS THANKS.

The waves are bigger than anything imaginable. Whole worlds within themselves.

Not dying is a source of constant surprise.

Every new breath unexpected.

Wetness is pretty much a given. Skin soaked, bone chilled, wet beyond
all previous measures of water saturation. We could wring my skin out to good effect.

And somehow the boat is still the right way up.

Moving.

All the things from beneath the waves that might eat me have so far chosen
Not to.

There are some things it pays not to question.
I do not want any of them to change their minds.

WELL, I HAVEN'T GOT ANY SILK, SO STRIPS OF OLD BED SHEET ARE GOING TO HAVE TO DO. AND I DON'T HAVE ANY INK MADE FROM GOAT'S BLOOD AND AMBERGRIS...
...WHAT IS THAT ANYWAY? I SUPPOSE JUST BLOOD OUGHT TO DO IT.
IT'S NOT LIKE I'VE GOT MUCH TO LOSE.
AND I'M PRETTY SURE LUNCH HAD BLOOD IN IT.

Chapter Eight
"Do you think anyone ever comes back?"

SALAMANDRA

...NO CHOICE. IT'S FOR THE BEST, I'M SURE YOU AGREE.
I THINK HE HAS A POINT...

... GUARD ME IN DARK PLACES ...GRANT ME THE BLESSINGS OF RAVENS AND THE COURAGE TO ENDURE. SQUIGGLE, SQUIGGLE... I WISH I KNEW WHAT HALF OF THESE THINGS MEANT. ALTHOUGH THAT ONE LOOKS A BIT LIKE A NOSE, AND THAT COULD BE A MUSHROOM.
WHAT ARE YOU DOING SALAMANDRA? IT'S LONG PASSED LIGHTS OUT.
NOTHING MUCH.
YOU'VE BEEN WRITING IN BLOOD AGAIN, HAVEN'T YOU?
ONLY A LITTLE BIT, AND IT IS MINE. IT'S NOT LIKE I BORROWED IT.

THAT REALLY ISN'T THE POINT. WE CAN'T GO ON LIKE THIS SALAMANDRA.

I KNOW. IT'S TIME FOR ME TO MOVE ON, ISN'T IT? THANKS FOR GIVING ME THIS LONG. I KNOW IT'S BEE HARD FOR YOU.

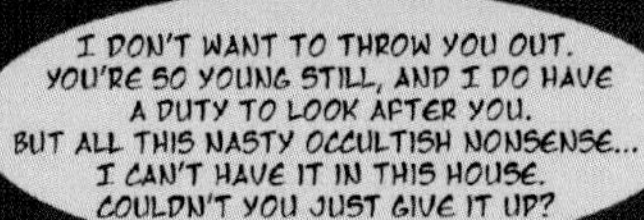
I DON'T WANT TO THROW YOU OUT. YOU'RE SO YOUNG STILL, AND I DO HAVE A DUTY TO LOOK AFTER YOU. BUT ALL THIS NASTY OCCULTISH NONSENSE... I CAN'T HAVE IT IN THIS HOUSE. COULDN'T YOU JUST GIVE IT UP?

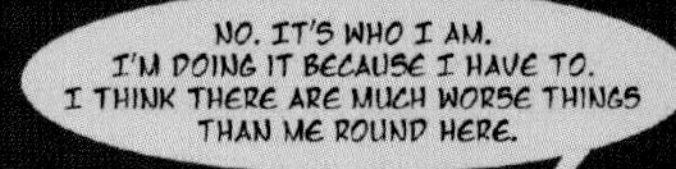
NO. IT'S WHO I AM. I'M DOING IT BECAUSE I HAVE TO. I THINK THERE ARE MUCH WORSE THINGS THAN ME ROUND HERE.

WHAT DO YOU MEAN?
LIKE THE WAY NO ONE CAN LEAVE?
MY SON LEFT.
IN RATHER UNUSUAL CIRCUMSTANCES.
I TRY NOT TO THINK ABOUT IT.
I'M FINDING IT HARD TO THINK ABOUT MUCH ELSE. HE IS OK THOUGH.
SALAMANDRA... ?
I SHOULD GO. THANKS AGAIN.

CHILDE SAL TO THE DARK TOWER CAME.

SO THERE IT IS CROW.
MY GRANDFATHER'S LEGACY.
I KNOW IT DOESN'T LOOK
VERY LIVEABLE IN RIGHT NOW,
BUT I'M SURE WE CAN FIX THAT.

THE MOON'S RISING, LOOK.

I HEARD YOU MOVED OUT OF THE ORPHANAGE.
YOU HEARD RIGHT. DO YOU WANT TO COME IN?
YOU'VE CHANGED THINGS.
I'D OFFER YOU A DRINK, BUT I THINK THERE'S SOMETHING LIVING IN THE KETTLE. OR THE KETTLE IS LIVING. IT'S BACK HERE.
WANT A HAND WITH THAT?
YES PLEASE.

AND..
I WAS WONDERING...
I'D LIKE TO LEARN
ABOUT WHAT YOU DO.
WOULD YOU TEACH ME?
PLEASE?
I DON'T THINK YOU'RE
GOING TO BE A WITCH.
I'M NOT,
BUT THERE ISN'T
ANYONE TO TEACH ME
HOW TO BE ME,
IS THERE?
YOU'VE GOT A
POINT HONEY.
I'LL SEE WHAT
I CAN DO.
THANKS.
SO THEY REALLY LEFT?
THEY REALLY DID.
WILL YOU TELL ME HOW
THEY DID IT?
I'VE SPENT MY WHOLE LIFE
TRYING TO FIGURE OUT
HOW TO GET OUT
OF THIS PLACE.

UMMM...
OH, I'M TOO OLD TO GO ANYWHERE NOW, TOO MUCH OF ME IS HERE.
I'M JUST CURIOUS.
OK. SOMETIME, I'LL TELL YOU.
DO YOU THINK ANYONE EVER COMES BACK?
THEY'D NEED THE SAME MAGIC. SO WHEN OWEN COMES BACK, I'LL BE IN THE RIGHT PLACE TO HELP HIM.
HE IS COMING BACK THEN?
COUNT ON IT.

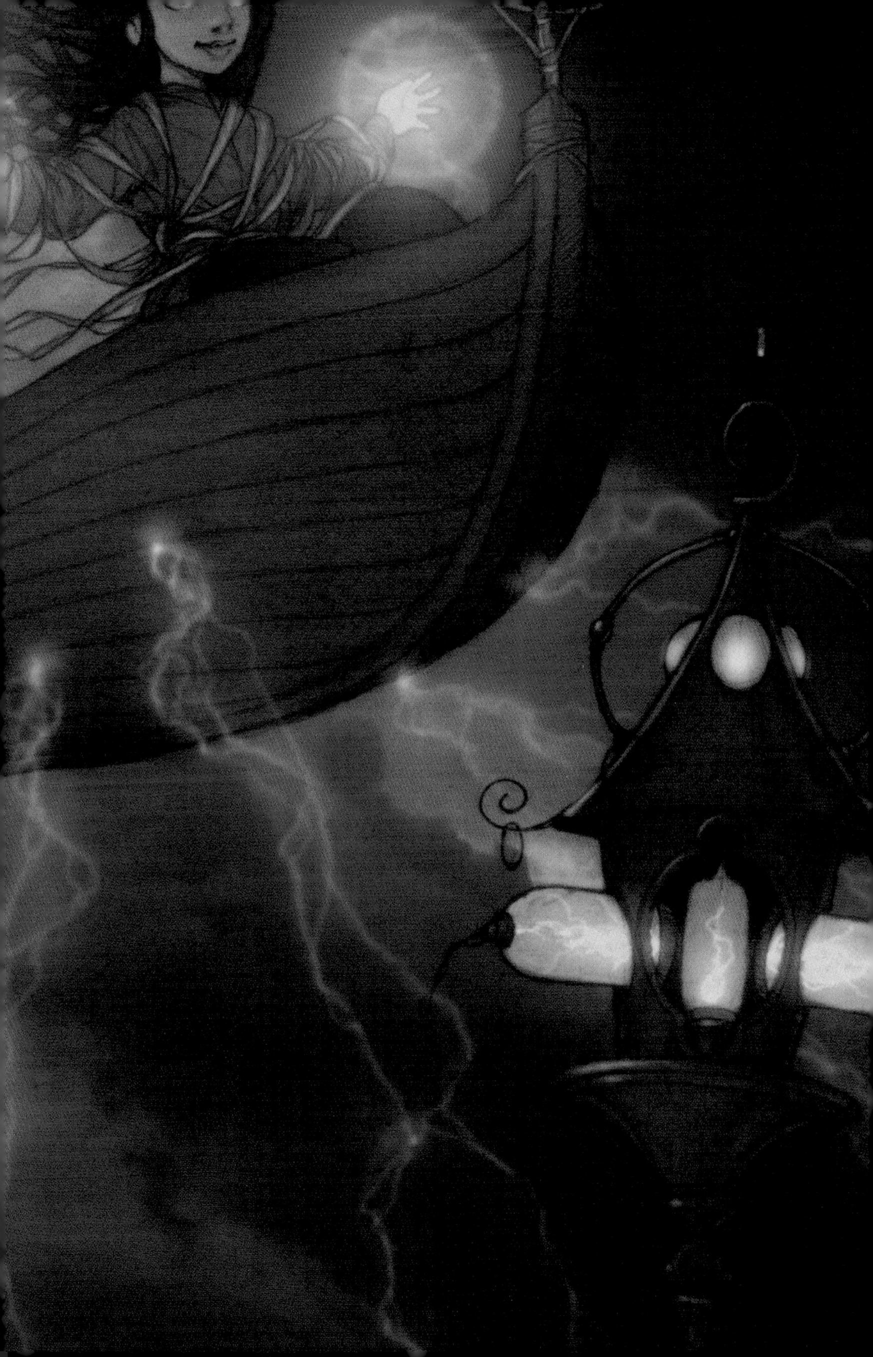

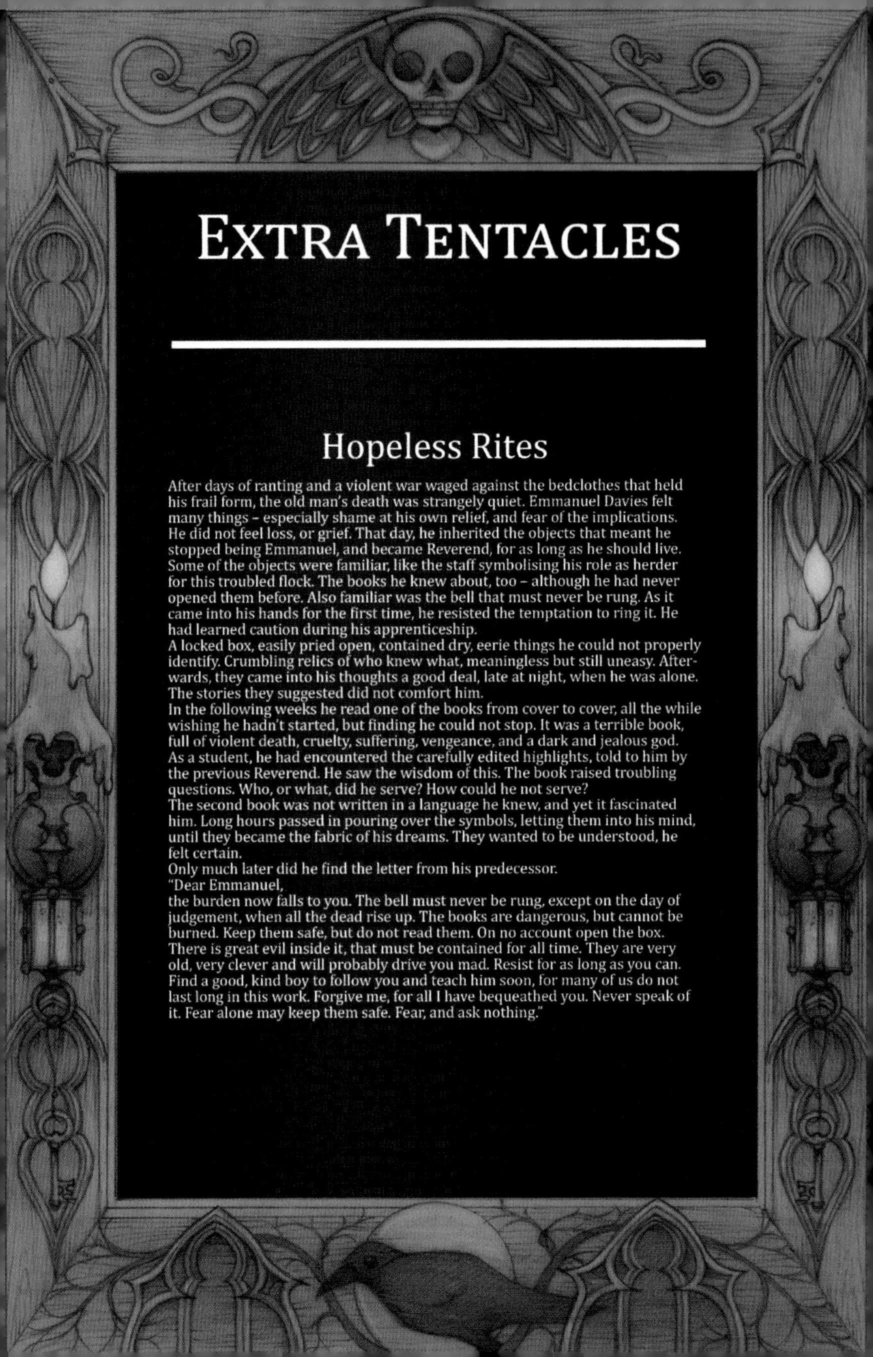

Extra Tentacles

Hopeless Rites

After days of ranting and a violent war waged against the bedclothes that held his frail form, the old man's death was strangely quiet. Emmanuel Davies felt many things – especially shame at his own relief, and fear of the implications. He did not feel loss, or grief. That day, he inherited the objects that meant he stopped being Emmanuel, and became Reverend, for as long as he should live. Some of the objects were familiar, like the staff symbolising his role as herder for this troubled flock. The books he knew about, too – although he had never opened them before. Also familiar was the bell that must never be rung. As it came into his hands for the first time, he resisted the temptation to ring it. He had learned caution during his apprenticeship.

A locked box, easily pried open, contained dry, eerie things he could not properly identify. Crumbling relics of who knew what, meaningless but still uneasy. Afterwards, they came into his thoughts a good deal, late at night, when he was alone. The stories they suggested did not comfort him.

In the following weeks he read one of the books from cover to cover, all the while wishing he hadn't started, but finding he could not stop. It was a terrible book, full of violent death, cruelty, suffering, vengeance, and a dark and jealous god. As a student, he had encountered the carefully edited highlights, told to him by the previous Reverend. He saw the wisdom of this. The book raised troubling questions. Who, or what, did he serve? How could he not serve?

The second book was not written in a language he knew, and yet it fascinated him. Long hours passed in pouring over the symbols, letting them into his mind, until they became the fabric of his dreams. They wanted to be understood, he felt certain.

Only much later did he find the letter from his predecessor.

"Dear Emmanuel,

the burden now falls to you. The bell must never be rung, except on the day of judgement, when all the dead rise up. The books are dangerous, but cannot be burned. Keep them safe, but do not read them. On no account open the box. There is great evil inside it, that must be contained for all time. They are very old, very clever and will probably drive you mad. Resist for as long as you can. Find a good, kind boy to follow you and teach him soon, for many of us do not last long in this work. Forgive me, for all I have bequeathed you. Never speak of it. Fear alone may keep them safe. Fear, and ask nothing."

Acknowledgements

Thank you, people who went the extra mile to help bring Hopeless into the world. Your support has been tremendous, and it just wouldn't be possible to do this sort of thing otherwise. It takes a large conceptual village to raise a graphic novel.

In no particular order...

Sarah Gothard, Simon and Marta La Thangue, Chandra Free, Francesca Dare, David Trott, Mark Rosher, Autumn Barlow, Colin McCracken, Emma Newman, Suna Dasi, Tom Sniegoski, Martin Pearson, Connie Reed, Paul Alborough, Mark Lawrence, Rebecca Wilson, Michelle Soulier, Barry Dodd, Brandan Kawashima, Greg Tulonen, Erik Moody, Cormac Brown, James Colvin, Sabrina Beckstead and Cynthia Beckstead, Phil and Jacqui Lovesey, Eric Orchard, Edric Edric, Walter Sickert, John Matthews, Rick Lowell at Casablanca Comics, everyone and Kendrick Street Art Gallery, everyone at Steampunk Weekend at Asylum, Nicolas Rossert and Charles Cutting at Sloth Comics, Lee Ann Faruga, Wren Tierneigh, Maxwell Vex

And in memory of Bill Baker.